Collins

Collins Revision

GCSE Foundation Chemistry

Revision Guide

FOR OCR GATEWAY B

About this book

This book covers GCSE Chemistry for OCR Gateway B at Foundation Level. Written by GCSE examiners, it is designed to help you to get the best grade in your GCSE Chemistry exams.
The book is divided into three parts; a topic-by-topic revision guide, workbook practice pages for each topic and detachable answers.

How to Use It

The revision guide section gives you complete coverage of each of the six modules that you need to study. Use it to build your knowledge and understanding.
The workbook section is packed with exam-style questions. Once you have covered a particular topic, use the matching workbook page to test yourself.
The answers in the back of the book are detachable. Remove them to help check your grade or a friend's.

Go Up a Grade

There are lots of revision guides for you to choose from. This one is different because it really helps you to go up a grade. Each topic in the revision guide and workbook sections is broken down and graded to show you what examiners look for at each level. This lets you check where you are, and see exactly what you need to do to improve your grade at every step. Crucially, it shows you what makes the difference between an E–F and a C–D grade answer.

Special Features

- **Questions** at the end of every topic page quickly test your level.
- **Top Tips** give you extra advice about what examiners really want.
- **Summaries** of each module remind you of the most important things to remember.
- **Checklists** for each module help you to monitor your progress.
- A comprehensive **glossary** gives you a quick reference guide to the Chemistry terms that you need to know.

Published by Collins
An imprint of HarperCollins*Publishers*
77–85 Fulham Palace Road
Hammersmith
London W6 8JB

Browse the complete Collins catalogue at
www.collinseducation.co.uk

10 9 8 7 6 5 4 3 2 1

ISBN-13 978-0-00-734808-4

British Library Cataloguing in Publication Data
A Catalogue record for this publication is available from the British Library

Written by Ann Daniels
Series Consultant Chris Sherry
Project Manager Charis Evans
Design and layout Graham Brasnett
Editor Mitch Fitton
Illustrated by Kathy Baxendale, IFA design Ltd, Mark Walker, Bob Lea and Steve Evans
Indexed by Marie Lorimer
Printed and bound in the UK by Martins the Printers, Berwick Upon Tweed

Acknowledgements
The Authors and Publishers are grateful to the following for permission to reproduce photographs:

Photos.com p5 TR & TL, Martyn F Chillmaid p5 BL, istock photo p5 BR, p10, p43, p59 TR, TL, BR, Science Photolibrary p18, p26 T, C & L, p28, p41, Maximilian Stock Ltd, p52, Sheila Terry, Science Photolibrary p55

Whilst every effort has been made to trace the copyright holders, in cases where this has been unsuccessful, or if any have inadvertently been overlooked, the Publishers will be pleased to make the necessary arrangements at the first opportunity.

Contents

1 H hydrogen 1

Key

relative atomic mass atomic symbol name atomic (proton) number

1	2											3	4	5	6	7	8
																	4 He helium 2
7 Li lithium 3	9 Be beryllium 4											11 B boron 5	12 C carbon 6	14 N nitrogen 7	16 O oxygen 8	19 F fluorine 9	20 Ne neon 10
23 Na sodium 11	24 Mg magnesium 12											27 Al aluminium 13	28 Si silicon 14	31 P phosphorus 15	32 S sulfur 16	35.5 Cl chlorine 17	40 Ar argon 18
39 K potassium 19	40 Ca calcium 20	45 Sc scandium 21	48 Ti titanium 22	51 V vanadium 23	52 Cr chromium 24	55 Mn manganese 25	56 Fe iron 26	59 Co cobalt 27	59 Ni nickel 28	63.5 Cu copper 29	65 Zn zinc 30	70 Ga gallium 31	73 Ge germanium 32	75 As arsenic 33	79 Se selenium 34	80 Br bromine 35	84 Kr krypton 36
85 Rb rubidium 37	88 Sr strontium 38	89 Y yttrium 39	91 Zr zirconium 40	93 Nb niobium 41	96 Mo molybdenum 42	[98] Tc technetium 43	101 Ru ruthenium 44	103 Rh rhodium 45	106 Pd palladium 46	108 Ag silver 47	112 Cd cadmium 48	115 In indium 49	119 Sn tin 50	122 Sb antimony 51	128 Te tellurium 52	127 I iodine 53	131 Xe xenon 54
133 Cs caesium 55	137 Ba barium 56	139 La* lanthanum 57	178 Hf hafnium 72	181 Ta tantalum 73	184 W tungsten 74	186 Re rhenium 75	190 Os osmium 76	192 Ir iridium 77	195 Pt platinum 78	197 Au gold 79	201 Hg mercury 80	204 Tl thallium 81	207 Pb lead 82	209 Bi bismuth 83	[209] Po polonium 84	[210] At astatine 85	[222] Rn radon 86
[223] Fr francium 87	[226] Ra radium 88	[227] Ac* actinium 89	[261] Rf rutherfordium 104	[262] Db dubnium 105	[266] Sg seaborgium 106	[264] Bh bohrium 107	[277] Hs hassium 108	[268] Mt meitnerium 109	[271] Ds darmstadtium 110	[272] Rg roentgenium 111	Elements with atomic numbers 112–116 have been reported but not fully authenticated.						

* The Lanthanides (atomic numbers 58–71) and the Actinides (atomic numbers 90–103) have been omitted.
Cu and Cl have not been rounded to the nearest whole number.

Cooking

Grades

Cooking food

G–E

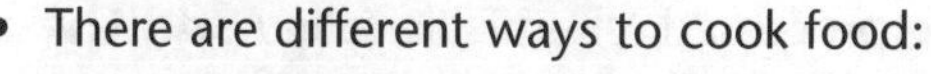

- There are different ways to cook food:
  - on a barbeque
  - on a grill
  - in a microwave
  - in an oven
  - on an electric or gas ring (frying, boiling or steaming).

Why do we cook chicken?

D–C

- Some foods can be eaten **raw**, but other foods must be **cooked** to make them safer or more attractive. Food is cooked because:
  - the high temperature **kills** harmful **microbes**
  - the **texture** is improved
  - the **taste** is improved
  - the **flavour** is enhanced
  - it's easier to **digest**.

Chemical changes

G–E

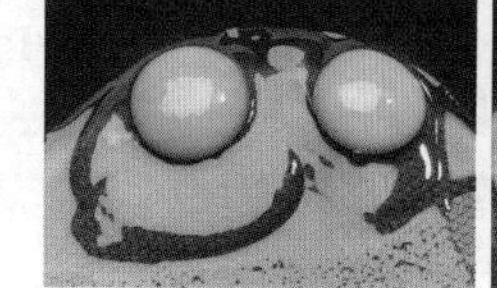
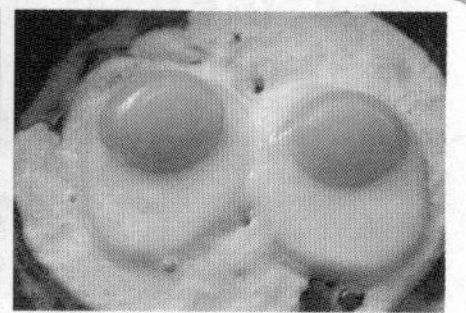

Eggs change irreversibly when they're cooked.

- When a food is heated and cooked, it **changes**. It can't go back to its raw state.

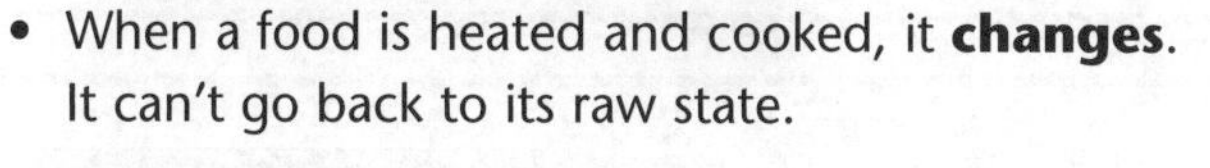

- Cooking food is a **chemical change** that's **irreversible**. An **energy change** takes place in the food and a **new substance** is made.
- When you cook **eggs**, the colourless, transparent liquid changes into a white, opaque solid.
- **Potatoes** must be cooked. When cooked, their taste and texture changes irreversibly.

D–C

- Potatoes and flour are good sources of **carbohydrate**.
- Meat and eggs are good sources of **proteins**. Proteins are large molecules that have definite shapes. When food is cooked, the protein molecules change shape.

Baking powder

G–E

- Baking powder gives off **carbon dioxide** that makes cakes rise when it's heated.

D–C

- Baking powder is a chemical called **sodium hydrogencarbonate**. When it's heated, it decomposes to give sodium carbonate, carbon dioxide and water:
  - the **reactant** is sodium hydrogencarbonate
  - the **products** are sodium carbonate, carbon dioxide and water.
- The word equation for the reaction is:

$$\text{sodium hydrogencarbonate} \xrightarrow{\text{heat}} \text{sodium carbonate} + \text{carbon dioxide} + \text{water}$$

Testing for carbon dioxide

G–E

- The chemical test for **carbon dioxide** is to pass it through **limewater**. It turns the limewater from colourless to milky white.

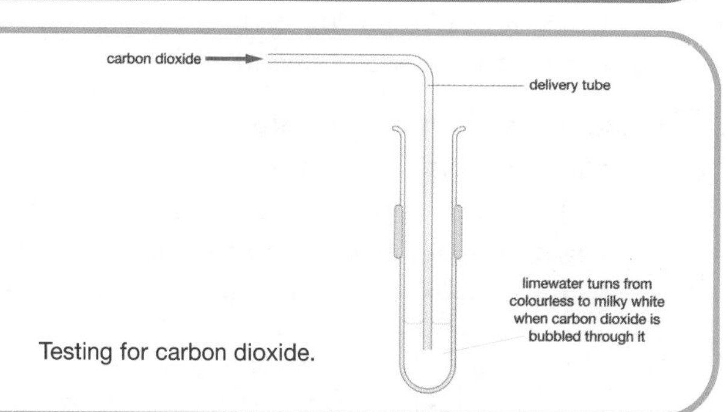

Testing for carbon dioxide.

Questions

Grades G-E

1 What does the word 'irreversible' mean?

Grades D-C

2 What do protein molecules do when they're heated?

3 When you heat baking powder it decomposes. What does this mean?

Grades G-E

4 What happens to limewater when carbon dioxide is bubbled through it?

Food additives

Grades

Food additives

G–E

- Foods contain many different **chemicals**. When foods are processed, chemicals called **additives** can be added. The main types of food additive are:
  - **antioxidants**
  - colours
  - **emulsifiers**
  - flavour enhancers.
- Antioxidants stop food from reacting with oxygen and turning bad.

D–C

- **Ascorbic acid** (vitamin C) is used in tinned fruit and wine as an antioxidant. Its E number is E300.
- Food additives are added for different reasons:
  - to **preserve** food by stopping it reacting with oxygen, bacteria or mould
  - to give a different **sensory experience**, such as to **enhance** the colour or flavour of food.

Food packaging

G–E

- **Labels** are now added to all foods that are sold. This makes sure that people know what they're buying and how much salt each product has. The ingredients are listed in descending order of their mass.

D–C

- Food packaging stops food **spoiling**.
  - **Active packaging** changes the condition of the food to extend its shelf life.
  - **Intelligent packaging** uses sensors to monitor the quality of the food and lets the customer know when the food is no longer fresh.
- These methods remove water, or heat or cool the contents of packs.

Nutrition		
Typical values	Per 30 g with 125 ml semi-skimmed milk	Per 100 g
Energy	738 kJ **174 kcal**	1624 kJ **383 kcal**
Protein	**5.8 g**	**5.5 g**
Carbohydrate	**31.7 g**	**84.8 g**
of which sugars	17.8 g	38.3 g
Fat	**2.7 g**	**2.4 g**
of which saturates	1.7 g	1.4 g
Fibre	**0.6 g**	**1.9 g**
Sodium	**0.6 g**	**1.4 g**

There are 84.8 g per 100 g of carbohydrate in this breakfast cereal.

Emulsions and emulsifiers

G–E

- Oil and water don't mix. If **washing-up liquid** is added, oily plates are easily cleaned. This is because oil doesn't attract water, it **repels** it.
- A detergent in washing-up liquid gives 'hooks' between oil and water. The oil is 'hooked' onto the water and pulled off a dirty plate. This is an example of an **emulsion**. The **detergent** in washing-up liquid acts as an **emulsifier**.

D–C

- Detergents are long molecules made up of two parts:
  - the **tail** is a 'fat-loving' part
  - the **head** is a 'water-loving' part.
- Examples of **emulsions** are:
  - some **paints**
  - **milk**, which is an emulsion of oil in water
  - **mayonnaise**, which is an emulsion of oil and vinegar with egg. Egg is the emulsifier.

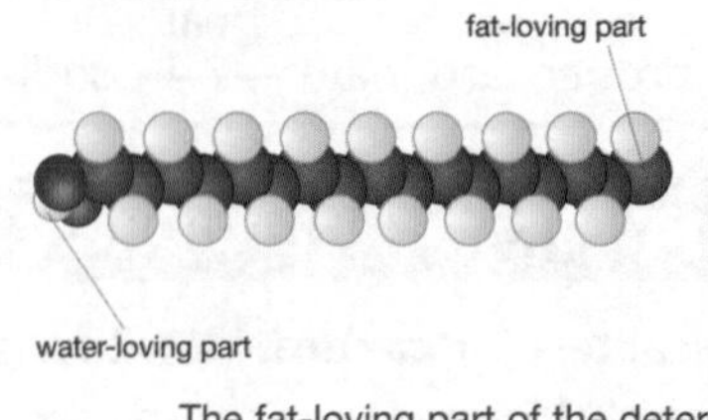

The fat-loving part of the detergent goes into the grease droplet.

Questions

Grades G-E

1 What's added to stop food reacting with oxygen?

Grades D-C

2 What's 'intelligent packaging'?

Grades G-E

3 What's used to help oil and water mix?

Grades D-C

4 Emulsifiers are long molecules that have two parts. Explain why.

Smells

Grades

Natural and synthetic cosmetics

G–E

- Perfumes and cosmetics can be made from **natural sources**.
- A similar perfume can be made **synthetically**. Chemicals are boiled to make an **ester**.
- Cosmetics must be tested to make sure they're safe. Some cosmetics are tested on animals, but some people strongly disagree with this.

D–C

- Cosmetics need to be thoroughly tested to ensure they don't cause rashes, itchiness, skin damage or lead to cancer or other life-threatening conditions.
- **Cosmetic testing** takes many years and is highly controversial.
  – Some people object to testing on animals as the animals may be harmed, and they don't have any control over what happens to them.
  – Other people say they feel safer if the cosmetics have been tested on animals.

Perfumes

G–E

- We can smell perfumes because they stimulate **sense cells** in the nose.
- This table shows the **properties** that a perfume needs:

D–C

need	evaporate easily	non-toxic	doesn't react with water	insoluble in water	doesn't irritate the skin
why	perfume particles reach nose	doesn't poison	doesn't react with perspiration	isn't washed off the skin	can be sprayed onto skin

Esters

D–C

- To make a perfume, **alcohol** is mixed with an **acid** to make an **ester**.
  alcohol + acid ⟶ ester + water
- Look at the diagram on the right.
  – Acid is added to the alcohol and is heated for some time.
  – The condenser stops the gas from escaping and helps it to cool down again.

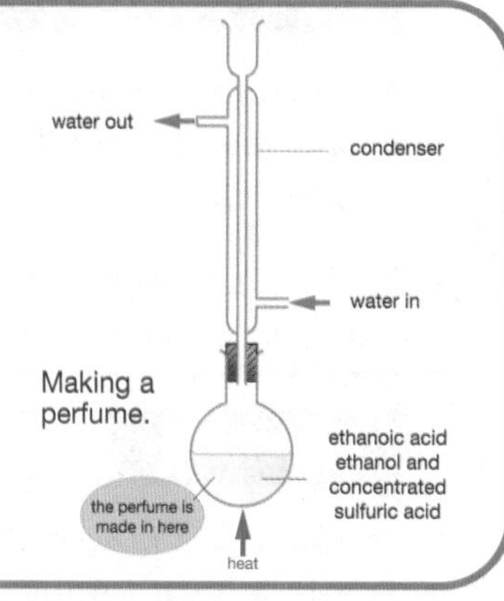

Making a perfume.

Solvents and solutions

G–E

- A substance that **dissolves** in a liquid is **soluble**. The substance is called the **solute** and the liquid that it dissolves in is called the **solvent**.
- A substance that doesn't dissolve in a liquid is **insoluble**.
  – Water doesn't dissolve nail varnish so can't be used to remove it from nails.
  – Nail varnish remover does dissolve nail varnish.

D–C

- A **solution** is a solute and a solvent that don't separate.
- Esters are used as solvents, and other solvents can be used as cleaners.

Questions

Grades G-E

1 What are the chemicals that make synthetic perfumes?

Grades D-C

2 Two different people may have different ideas about cosmetic testing. Explain why.

3 Which two substances combine to make an ester?

Grades G-E

4 When a solute dissolves in a solvent, it's said to be ____________________.

Making crude oil useful

Fossil fuels

- Coal, gas and crude oil are **fossil fuels**. Fossil fuels have formed from dead animals and plants trapped in the Earth and compressed over millions of years. When these fossil fuels are used up, there will be no more. They're **non-renewable**.
- Fossil fuels are **finite resources** because they're no longer being made.

Fractional distillation

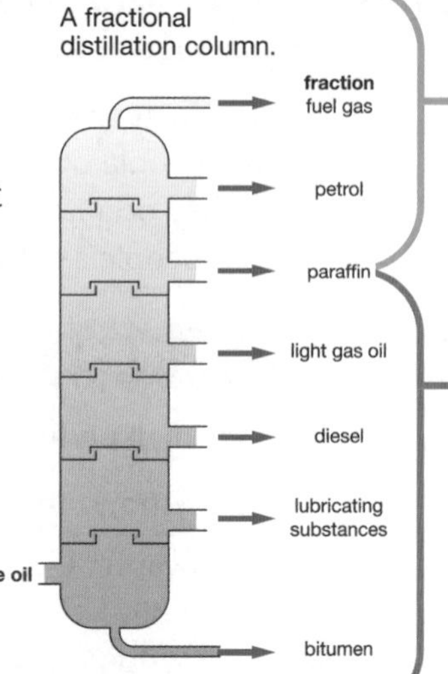
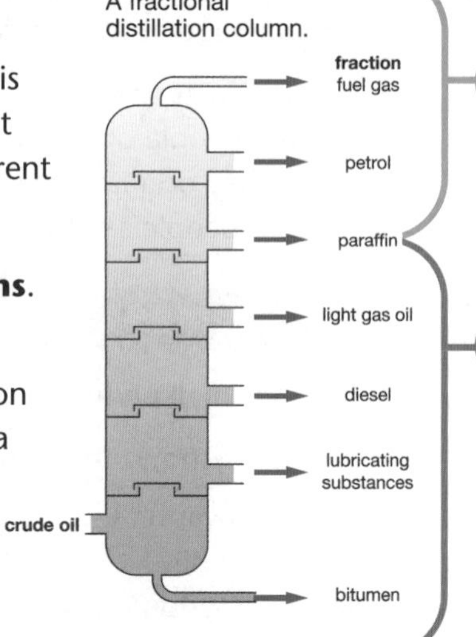

A fractional distillation column.

- Crude oil is separated by heating it up and then cooling it down. This is called **fractional distillation**. The crude oil is separated into different **fractions** (parts). The process works because each fraction has a different **boiling point**.
- Crude oil is a mixture of many types of oil, which are all **hydrocarbons**.
- In fractional distillation, crude oil is heated at the bottom of a tower.
  – Oil that doesn't boil, sinks as a thick liquid to the bottom. This fraction is **bitumen** and is used to make **tar** for road surfaces. Bitumen has a very high boiling point. It 'exits' at the bottom of the tower.
  – Other fractions boil and their gases rise up the tower. Fractions with lower boiling points, such as **petrol** and **LPG**, 'exit' at the top of the tower, where it's colder.

Problems in extracting crude oil

- When crude oil is found, it comes through the Earth's crust on land or under the sea. This is a dangerous activity. If sea-going tankers run aground and are damaged, the spilt oil forms an **oil slick**.
- Oil slicks can harm animals, pollute beaches and destroy unique habitats. Clean-up operations are extremely expensive and the detergents and barrages used can cause **environmental problems**.

Cracking

Cracking.

- **Cracking** is a process that:
  – needs a **high temperature**
  – needs a **catalyst**
  – turns less useful large hydrocarbon molecules (i.e. paraffin) into more useful smaller hydrocarbon molecules (i.e. petrol).
- Cracking is a process that:
  – turns large alkane molecules into smaller alkane and alkene molecules
  – also makes useful alkene molecules, which can be used to make **polymers**.
- Alkanes have a general formula of: C_nH_{2n+2}.

Octane has 8 carbon atoms and $2n + 2 = 18$ hydrogen atoms. The formula for octane is C_8H_{18}.

Questions

Grades G-E

1 What's a fossil fuel?

Grades D-C

2 Where do fractions with the lowest boiling points 'exit' the tower in fractional distillation?

Grades G-E

3 Explain what's meant by the process 'cracking'.

Grades D-C

4 What's the formula for an alkane with 7 carbon atoms?

Making polymers

Polymers and polymerisation

G–E

- A polymer is a very **big molecule** made up of many small molecules, called **monomers**, joined together in a **chain**. This reaction is called **polymerisation**.

D–C

- You can recognise a polymer from its **displayed formula** by looking out for these features:
  - a long chain
  - the pattern repeats every two carbon atoms
  - there are two brackets on the end with extended bonds through them
  - there's an '*n*' after the brackets.

This is the displayed formula of poly(ethene).

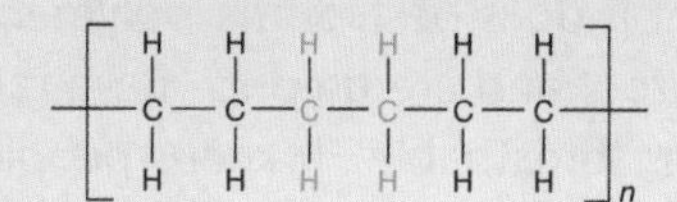

- A **polymerisation reaction** needs **high pressure** and a **catalyst**.
- When a polymer is made from monomers that are the same type, it's called an **addition polymer**.

Hydrocarbons

G–E

- A **hydrocarbon** is made up of **carbon** and **hydrogen** only. **Alkanes** and **alkenes** are hydrocarbons.
- You can recognise a hydrocarbon from its displayed formula as it only has C or H joined together.

One atom of carbon and four atoms of hydrogen chemically combine to make a **hydrocarbon** called **methane**.

CH_4

- If the name of the alkane is known, it's easy to predict the name of the alkene.

number of carbon atoms	alkane	displayed formula	alkene	displayed formula
2	ethane	H–C–C–H (each C with H above and below)	ethene	$H_2C=CH_2$
3	propane	H–C–C–C–H (each C with H above and below)	propene	H–C=C–C–H

D–C

- A hydrocarbon is a compound of carbon and hydrogen atoms only.
  - An **alkane** has a single bond C–C.
  - An **alkene** has one double bond C=C.

Propane, C_3H_8, is a hydrocarbon and an **alkane**.

Propanol, C_3H_7OH, *isn't* a hydrocarbon because it contains an oxygen atom.

Propene is a hydrocarbon, a **monomer** and an **alkene**.

Polypropene is the **polymer** made.

Questions

Grades G-E

1 Write down the name of the polymer made from the monomer styrene.

Grades D-C

2 What two conditions are needed for polymerisation to take place?

Grades G-E

3 What's the name of the alkane that has two carbon atoms?

Grades D-C

4 What's the difference between an alkane and an alkene?

Designer polymers

Grades

Uses of polymers

G–E

- Fabrics for clothes, paint for cars and cases for computers are all made from different **polymers**. Polymers are **chemicals** such as poly(ethene), nylon and polyester.

clothes carrier bags packaging rope

Polymers are chosen for the job they do best.

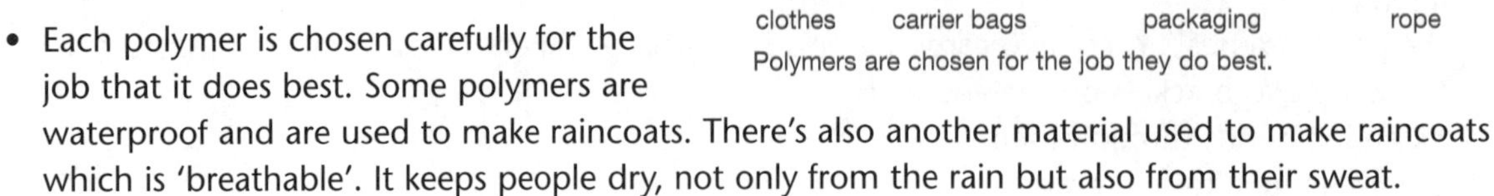

- Each polymer is chosen carefully for the job that it does best. Some polymers are waterproof and are used to make raincoats. There's also another material used to make raincoats which is 'breathable'. It keeps people dry, not only from the rain but also from their sweat.

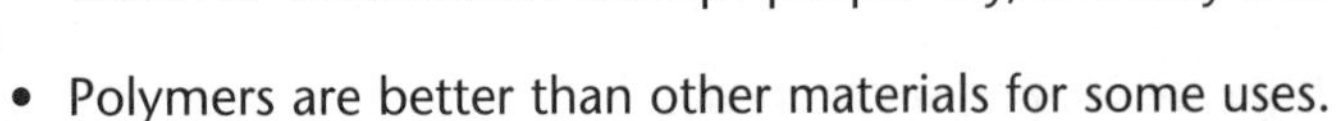

- Polymers are better than other materials for some uses.

D–C

use	polymer	other material
contact lens	wet on the eye	dry on the eye
teeth filling	attractive	looks metallic
wound dressing	waterproof	gets wet

Waterproof walking.

- **Nylon** is tough, lightweight and keeps rainwater out, but it keeps body sweat in. The water vapour from the sweat **condenses** and makes the wearer wet and cold inside their raincoat.
- If nylon is **laminated** with a PTFE/polyurethane **membrane**, clothing can be made that's waterproof and breathable. Gore-Tex® has all the properties of nylon and is breathable, so it's worn by many active outdoor people. Water vapour from sweat can pass through the membrane, but rainwater can't.

Disposing of polymers

- Most **addition polymers** are **non-biodegradable**. They don't decay and aren't decomposed by bacteria.
- They can be disposed of in **landfill sites**, by **burning** and by **recycling**. However, they're difficult to dispose of and can cause litter and pollution.

- **Disposal problems** for non-biodegradable polymers include the following:
  – landfill sites get filled quickly and waste valuable land
  – burning waste plastics produces toxic gases
  – disposal by burning or landfill sites wastes a valuable resource
  – problems in sorting different polymers makes recycling difficult.
- Scientists are developing addition polymers that are **biodegradable**. These are easily disposed of by **dissolving**. Biopol is a biodegradeable plastic that can be used to make laundry bags for hospitals. It degrades when washed leaving the laundry in the machine.

Questions

Grades G-E

1 What two properties are needed in a polymer to make drainpipes?

Grades D-C

2 What's the disadvantage of using nylon to make outdoor clothes?

Grades G-E

3 What does non-biodegradable mean?

Grades D-C

4 What's given off when disposing of plastics by burning?

Using carbon fuels

Choosing a fuel

G–E

- Coal isn't a good fuel for a motor vehicle! **Petrol** or **diesel** are good **fuels** for cars because they're liquids. They flow round the engine easily.

D–C

- A fuel is chosen because of its **characteristics**.

characteristic	**coal**	**petrol**
energy value	high	high
availability	good	good
storage	bulky and dirty	volatile
toxicity	produces acid fumes	produces less acid fumes
pollution caused	acid rain, carbon dioxide and soot	carbon dioxide, nitrous oxides

Combustion

G–E

- **Oxygen** is needed for fuels to burn. Burning is called **combustion**.
- Combustion releases **useful heat energy**.
- Lots of oxygen is needed for **complete combustion**.
- Complete combustion of a **hydrocarbon fuel** makes **carbon dioxide** and **water**.
- If a fuel burns in a **shortage of oxygen**, it's called **incomplete combustion**. Unwanted gases are given off that contain **soot** and are **toxic**.
- One of the toxic **fumes** is a gas called **carbon monoxide**. This is a **poisonous** gas.
- A **Bunsen burner** flame produces **energy** from burning gas.
  - If the air hole is **open**, a **blue** flame is seen. The fuel is burning in **plenty of oxygen**: combustion is complete.
  - If the air hole is **closed**, a **yellow** flame is seen. The fuel is burning in a **shortage of oxygen**: combustion is incomplete.

Top Tip!

Complete combustion gives off **carbon dioxide** and **water**. **Incomplete** combustion gives off **carbon monoxide** and **water**.

D–C

- The word equation for a fuel burning in air is:
  fuel + oxygen ⟶ carbon dioxide + water
- This reaction can be shown by an experiment in the laboratory.
  - **Cobalt chloride** paper or **white copper sulphate** powder is used to test for water.
  - **Limewater** is used to test for carbon dioxide.
- Complete combustion is better than incomplete combustion because:
  - less soot is made
  - more heat energy is released
  - toxic carbon monoxide gas isn't produced.

When a fuel burns in air, what's produced?

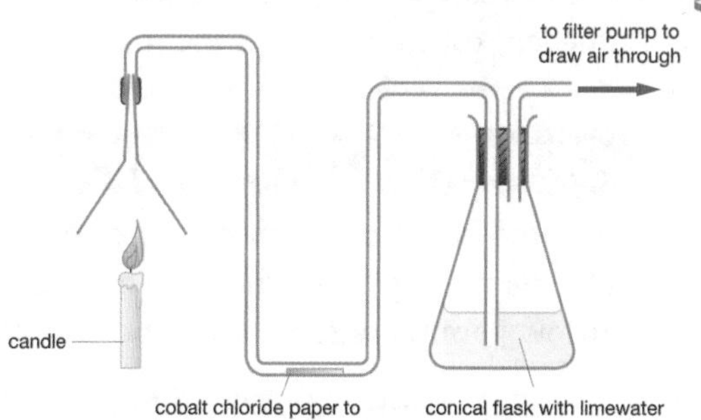

Top Tip!

Remember: gas appliances should be checked regularly! A heater in a poorly ventilated room is burning fuel in a shortage of oxygen. It will give off poisonous carbon monoxide.

Questions

Grades G-E

1 What gas is needed for fuels to burn?

2 Which colour flame in a Bunsen burner releases more useful energy?

Grades D-C

3 Which liquid is used to test for carbon dioxide?

4 Complete combustion is better than incomplete combustion. Explain why.

Energy

Grades

Chemical reactions

G–E

> **Top Tip!**
> Remember that:
> – energy is measured in joules (J)
> – temperature is measured in degree Celsius (°C).

- **Chemical reactions** can make:
  - heat
  - light
  - sound
  - electricity.
- A chemical reaction happens when **reactants** change into **products**.
- If things get hotter or cooler, **energy** has been transferred.

D–C

- Chemical reactions can be divided into two groups.
  - When energy is **transferred** to the surroundings in a chemical reaction, it's an **exothermic** reaction (energy is released). This is shown by a **temperature increase**, for example a lit firework.
  - When energy is **taken from** the surroundings in a chemical reaction, it's an **endothermic** reaction (absorbs energy). This is shown by a **temperature decrease**, for example in photosynthesis.

Fuels

G–E

- **Fuels** need oxygen to burn.
- **Ethanol** burns in oxygen to make carbon dioxide and water:
  - the **reactants** are ethanol and oxygen
  - the **products** are carbon dioxide and water.

  ethanol + oxygen ⟶ carbon dioxide + water
- You could use this experiment to compare two different fuels.
  - Place the same mass of fuel in two spirit burners.
  - Place the same mass of water in two test tubes.
  - When all the fuel has burnt, measure the increase in temperature of the water in each test tube using a thermometer.

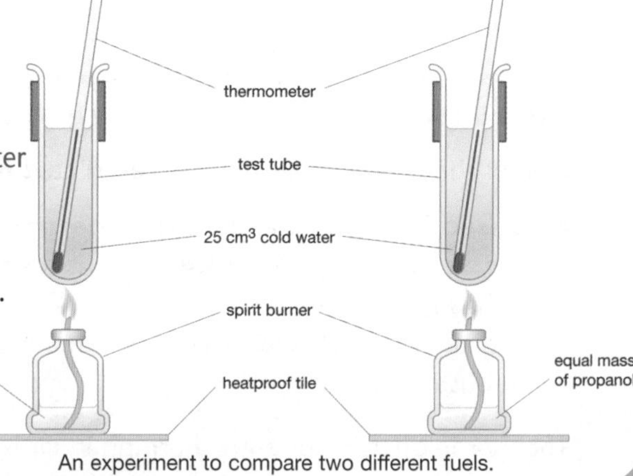

An experiment to compare two different fuels.

Comparing the energy from different flames

D–C

- The flame of a Bunsen burner changes colour depending on the amount of oxygen it burns in.
  - Blue flames are seen when the gas burns in plenty of oxygen (**complete combustion**).
  - Yellow flames are seen when the gas burns in limited oxygen (**incomplete combustion**).
- You need to know how to design your own experiment to compare the energy transferred in the two different flames. Here are some hints:
  - remember the apparatus used to compare fuels
  - the amount of gas used needs to be measured
  - remember to make the tests fair.

Questions

Grades G-E

1 Name two types of energy that can be made during a chemical reaction.

Grades D-C

2 What's an exothermic reaction?

Grades G-E

3 Name two things that must be kept constant (stay the same) to make it a fair test when you compare fuels by heating water.

Grades D-C

4 What type of flame is seen during incomplete combustion?

C1 Summary

Food and additives

All foods are chemicals. Cooking is a **chemical change**. A chemical change is irreversible and a new substance is made.

Intelligent packaging helps with storage of food.

Oil and water don't mix. **Emulsifiers** help water and oil to mix. Emulsifiers have a water-loving end and a water-hating end.

Egg and meat are **proteins**. Proteins in eggs and meat change shape when cooked.

Food is cooked to:
- **kill microbes**
- improve **texture**
- improve **flavour**
- make it **easier to digest**.

Additives may be added as:
- **antioxidants**
- **colours**
- **emulsifiers**
- **flavour enhancers**.

Smells and crude oil

Perfumes are **esters** that can be made from acids and alcohols. Perfumes must evaporate easily and be non-toxic.

Crude oil is separated by **fractional distillation**. The fractions with the lower boiling points exit at the top of the tower.

Crude oil is a **fossil fuel** made by dead animals being compressed over millions of years. It's **non-renewable**.

Nail varnish doesn't dissolve in water but it does in remover. Solutes **dissolve** in solvents to make solutions.

There's not enough petrol made to meet the demand. There's more heavy oil distilled than needed. These **larger alkane molecules** can be cracked to make smaller, more useful ones, like those of petrol.

Polymers

Polymers are large, long-chain molecules made from small monomers.

Nylon and Gore-Tex® can be used in coats because they're **waterproof**. Gore-Tex® has the advantage that it's also **breathable**.

Monomers are **alkenes**, such as ethene and propene. Alkenes are **hydrocarbons** made of carbon and hydrogen only.

Poly(ethene) is used for plastic bags because it's waterproof and flexible. **Poly(styrene)** is used for packaging and insulation.

Fossil fuels and energy

If there's a good supply of oxygen, there's **complete combustion**. If not, there's **incomplete combustion**.

An **exothermic** reaction **transfers heat out** to the surroundings. An **endothermic** reaction **transfers heat in**.

When choosing a fuel to use for a particular purpose, several factors need to be considered:
- energy value and availability
- storage and cost
- toxicity and how much pollution they cause
- how easy they're to use.

Fuels can be compared by using the same mass of fuel to heat a fixed amount of water and **measuring the change in temperature**.

Grades

Paints and pigments

What is paint?

G–E

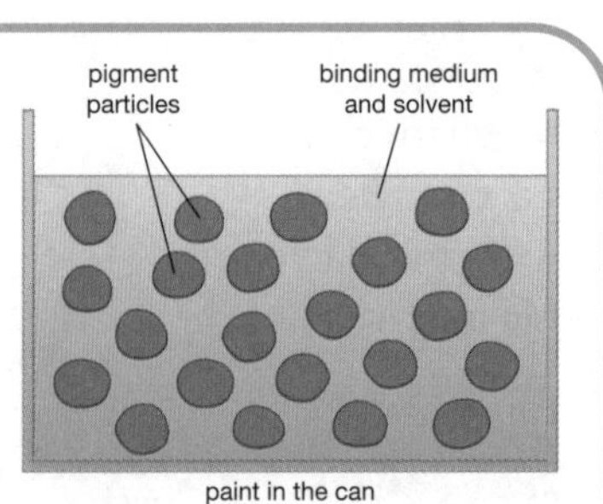

paint in the can

- Paint is a mixture called a **colloid**. The ingredients of paint are:
  - a **pigment** – a coloured substance often made of ground-up rock
  - a **binding medium** – glue or oil
  - a **solvent** – thins the paint, making it easier to use.
- In oil paints:
  - the pigment is spread in oil
  - the oil is dissolved in a solvent if it's too thick.
- We use paints:
  - to **protect** wood against rain; the oil sticks to the wood and forms a skin
  - to **decorate** pictures or walls in a house; the binder is used to stick the pigment to the canvas or walls.

D–C

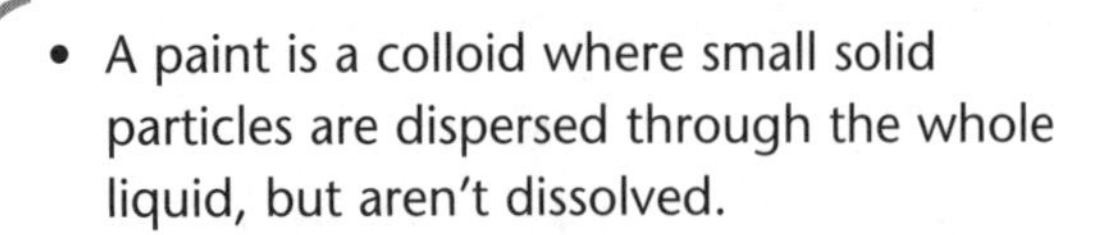

- A paint is a colloid where small solid particles are dispersed through the whole liquid, but aren't dissolved.

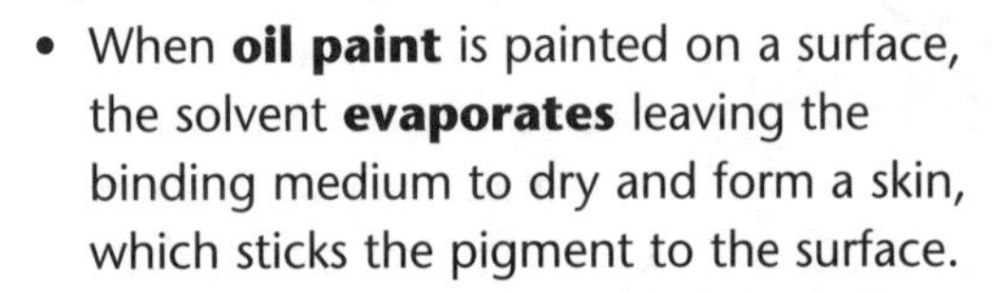

- When **oil paint** is painted on a surface, the solvent **evaporates** leaving the binding medium to dry and form a skin, which sticks the pigment to the surface.
- An **emulsion paint** is a water-based paint. It's made of tiny droplets of one liquid in water, which is called an **emulsion**. When emulsion paint has been painted on to a surface as a thin layer, the water evaporates leaving the binding medium and pigment behind. As it dries it joins together to make a continuous film.

Pigments

G–E

- Two types of pigment are shown in the table.

thermochromic pigment	phosphorescent pigment
when it gets hot, it changes colour	takes in light energy during the day
when it cools down, it changes back to the original colour	gives out light energy at night
used in some paints that are chosen for their colour and also for the temperature at which their colour changes, e.g. a thermochromic pigment that changes colour at 45 °C can be used to paint cups or kettles to act as a warning	stores the energy that it absorbs and can release it slowly as light

D–C

Dyes

G–E

- Dyes are used to colour fabrics. Some dyes are **natural** such as juice from coloured berries. Others are **synthetic** and made from chemicals.

D–C

- Synthetic dyes have increased the number of colours available.

Questions

Grades G-E

1 What's the job of a solvent in paint?

Grades D-C

2 What's a colloid?

Grades G-E

3 What's a thermochromic pigment?

Grades D-C

4 The range of colours for fabrics has increased over the past 150 years. Explain why.

Construction materials

Grades

The raw materials

G–E

- These materials are used in construction:
  - granite, marble and limestone
  - aluminium and iron (steel)
  - brick, cement, concrete and glass.

D–C

- Limestone is easier to cut into blocks than marble or granite. Marble is much harder than limestone. Granite is harder still and is very difficult to shape.
- Brick, concrete, steel, aluminium and glass come from materials in the ground, but they need to be manufactured from raw materials. This is shown in the table.

raw material	clay	limestone and clay	sand	iron ore	aluminium ore
building material	brick	cement	glass	iron	aluminium

Mining and quarrying

G–E

- Many modern buildings are made from materials dug out of the Earth.
- Stone such as **limestone**, **marble** and **granite** is cut out of the ground and used in buildings. Blocks of stone are expensive to quarry and are only used for special buildings.
- There are many environmental problems caused by removing rocks from the ground:
  - quarries and mines take up land-space
  - quarrying means an increase in noise, traffic and dust
  - landscapes are destroyed and have to be reconstructed.

Cement and concrete

G–E

- Limestone and marble are both forms of **calcium carbonate**. When calcium carbonate is heated, it **thermally decomposes** to form **calcium oxide** and **carbon dioxide**.
- **Cement** is made from limestone. To make cement, the limestone is heated and clay is added.
- **Concrete** is made when cement, sand and gravel are mixed with water and left to set.
- Concrete can be **reinforced**. It has steel rods inside it and is much stronger than normal concrete. The concrete is poured around steel rods and left to set.

D–C

- Calcium carbonate thermally decomposes at a very high temperature. This is shown in the word equation:

$$\text{calcium carbonate} \xrightarrow{\text{heat}} \text{calcium oxide} + \text{carbon dioxide}$$

- **Thermal decomposition** is the chemical breakdown of a compound into at least two other compounds under the effect of heat.
- **Cement** is made when limestone and clay are heated together.
- Reinforced concrete has steel rods or steel meshes running through it and is stronger than concrete. It is a **composite** material.

Questions

Grades G-E

1 Name three construction materials.

Grades D-C

2 What's cement made from?

Grades G-E

3 What's the chemical name for marble and limestone?

Grades D-C

4 What are the products of heating limestone?

Does the Earth move?

Grades

The structure of the Earth

G–E

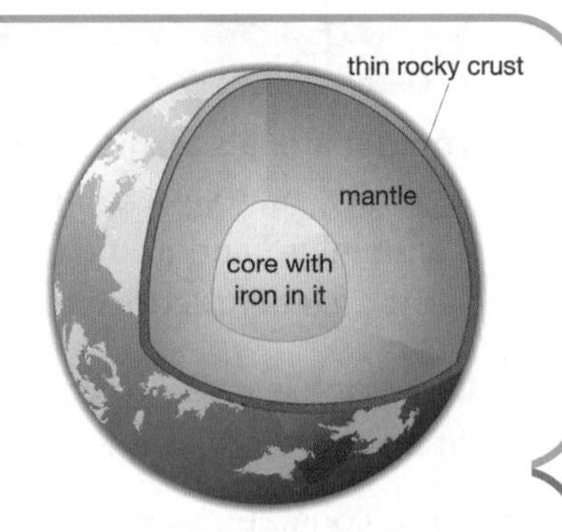

- The Earth is a sphere with an **iron core** surrounded by a **mantle**. On the outside is a thin, rocky **crust**. The mantle is made of molten rock.
- The outer layer of the Earth is made of **tectonic plates**, which move very slowly over the molten rock. At the **plate boundaries** this movement causes **earthquakes** and **volcanoes**.

D–C

- The outer layer of the Earth is called the **lithosphere**. It's relatively cold and rigid and is made of the crust and the part of the mantle that lies just underneath.
- The tectonic plates that make up the Earth's crust are **less dense** than the mantle, which they 'float' on. There are two kinds of plate:
  - **continental plates** that carry the continents
  - **oceanic plates** that lie underneath the oceans.

oceanic plate
continental plate
upper mantle
crust
lithosphere

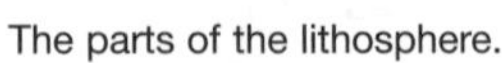
The parts of the lithosphere.

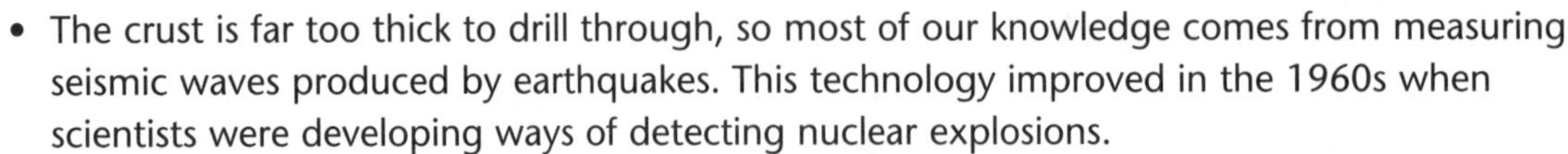

- The crust is far too thick to drill through, so most of our knowledge comes from measuring seismic waves produced by earthquakes. This technology improved in the 1960s when scientists were developing ways of detecting nuclear explosions.

Magma and rocks

G–E

- Underneath the surface of the Earth, most of the rock is solid. However, some of the rock does melt and is called **magma**. It slowly moves up to the surface of the Earth. Eventually it cools down and **solidifies** to make **igneous** rock.
- **Molten rock** that reaches the surface of the Earth through weaknesses is called **lava**. It comes out in a **volcano**.
  - Volcanoes that produce runny lava are often fairly safe.
  - If the lava is thick and sticky then an eruption can be explosive.
  - The ash from volcanoes makes a rich soil that's good for growing things.
  - Most volcanic eruptions aren't that dangerous, so people think it's worth moving back to the area.

D–C

- Magma rises through the Earth's crust because it's less dense than the crust. It cools and solidifies into igneous rock either after it comes out of a volcano as lava, or before it even gets to the surface.
- By looking at crystals of **igneous rock**, geologists can tell how quickly the rock cooled.
  - Igneous rock that **cools rapidly** (close to the surface) has small crystals.
  - Igneous rock that **cools slowly** (further from the surface and better insulated) has large crystals.

rock type	small crystal	large crystal
iron-rich magma	basalt	gabbro
silica-rich magma	rhyolite	granite

- Geologists study volcanic rocks to decide what previous eruptions were like. They also use seismic measurements to help them predict future eruptions and learn more about the Earth's structure.

Questions

Grades G-E

1 The Earth is made up of three parts. Name them.

Grades D-C

2 Why do the tectonic plates 'float' on the molten rock?

Grades G-E

3 What type of rock is made when magma cools down?

Grades D-C

4 Explain why the size of crystals changes when magma cools.

Grades

Metals and alloys

Copper

G–E

- Rocks containing copper ore are mined. Copper is a metal **element**. An ore is a **compound**.
- In the **laboratory**, copper is extracted from its ore by heating it with **carbon**.
- **Electrolysis** is used to purify copper.
- More than a third of all copper is **recycled**, saving resources and money.
  - It's cheaper to recycle copper than to extract new copper from the ground.
  - Recycling also saves energy needed to crush rock and to operate smelters and electrolysis cells.

D–C

- Copper has a fairly **low melting point** that makes it easy to melt down and recycle. However, copper that's been used already may be contaminated with other elements, such as solder. This means that it can't be used for purposes where the copper must be very pure, such as electric wiring.
- Copper used for recycling has to be sorted carefully so that valuable 'pure' copper scrap isn't mixed with less pure scrap.
- When impure copper is used to make **alloys**, it must first be analysed to find out how much of each element is present. If the scrap copper is very impure, it has to be electrolysed again before it can be used.

Electrolysis

D–C

- Impure copper can be purified in the laboratory using an **electrolysis cell**.
  - The **anode** is impure copper and dissolves into the **electrolyte**.
  - The **cathode** is 'plated' with new copper.

DC power supply
\-
\+
impure anode dissolves
electrolyte
cathode plated with copper
impurities

An electrolysis cell.

Alloys

G–E

- An **alloy** is a mixture of a metal element with another element.
- By adding another element to a metal its properties can be changed to make it more useful. For example, **steel** is a useful alloy of **iron**.
- Examples of alloys are: amalgam, brass, bronze, solder and steel.
  - **Amalgam** is used by dentists to fill cavities in teeth.
  - **Brass** is used to make taps and door handles.
  - **Solder** is used to join metals.

D–C

- Most **metals** form alloys.
  - Amalgam contains mercury.
  - Brass contains copper and zinc.
  - Solder contains lead and tin.

Top Tip!

Alloys are often more useful than the metals they're made from.

Questions

Grades G-E

1 Copper is recycled where possible. Explain why.

Grades D-C

2 Which electrode becomes pure copper in electrolysis?

Grades G-E

3 What's an alloy?

Grades D-C

4 Which metals form the alloy brass?

Cars for scrap

Rusting and corrosion

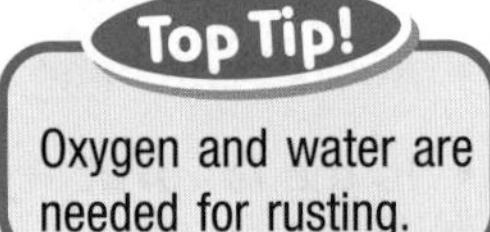

G–E

- **Rust** is a brownish solid that forms when iron is in contact with **oxygen** and **water**. Rust flakes off the surface of the iron.
- Most cars have a metal body made of steel or aluminium.
  – **Steel** is an **alloy** that contains mostly iron; all cars made with steel rust.
  – Cars made with **aluminium** don't **corrode** when oxygen and water are present.

D–C

- **Acid rain** and **salt water** accelerate rusting.
- Aluminium doesn't corrode in moist air because it has a protective layer of **aluminium oxide** which doesn't flake off the surface.

Materials and their properties

G–E

- A material is chosen because of its **properties**. For example, a car is made of: **metals** and **alloys** (copper, iron, steel, lead and aluminium), **plastics**, **glass** and **fibres**.
- **Aluminium** and **iron** are: good **conductors** of **electricity**; **malleable** (easily beaten into thin sheets); and not very strong (they only become strong when they're made into **alloys**).
- There are important differences between aluminium and iron:
  – it's easy to separate iron from aluminium because iron is magnetic and aluminium isn't
  – iron is more dense than aluminium
  – iron corrodes easily and aluminium doesn't.

D–C

- Alloys often have different and more useful properties than the pure metals they're made from. **Steel** (an alloy made of iron and carbon) is stronger and harder than iron and doesn't rust as easily as pure iron.
- Steel and aluminium can both be used to make **car bodies**, but each material has its advantages:
  – iron is stronger and harder – aluminium is lighter – aluminium corrodes less.

Recycling

Recycling car material using an electromagnet.

- The advantages of recycling in the car industry are:
  – aluminium and iron are **finite resources** (they will eventually run out)
  – it avoids environmental damage due to mining and quarrying
  – it reduces the amount of rubbish that goes into landfill sites

D–C

  – more recycling of metals means that less metal ore needs to be mined
  – recycling of iron and aluminium saves money and energy compared to making them from their ores.
- European Union law requires 85% (increasing to 95% in the future) of a car to be recyclable. Technology has to be developed to separate all the different materials used in making a car.
- Benefits of recycling other materials used in a car include:
  – less crude oil is used to make **plastics** and less non-biodegradeable waste is dumped
  – recycling **batteries** reduces the dumping of toxic materials into the environment.

Questions

Grades G-E

1 Which two chemicals are both needed for iron to rust?

Grades D-C

2 Explain how aluminium is protected from corrosion in moist air.

Grades G-E

3 Which metal is more dense: iron or aluminium?

Grades D-C

4 Give two reasons why a car should be made from aluminium.

Clean air

Clean air

G–E

- **Air** is a mixture of different gases:
  – **oxygen** – **nitrogen** – **water vapour** – **carbon dioxide**
- The amount of water vapour in the air changes, but the amounts of the other gases in the air remain almost constant.
- The levels of gases in the air depend on:
  – **combustion** and **respiration**, which increase the level of carbon dioxide and decrease the level of oxygen
  – **photosynthesis**, which decreases the level of carbon dioxide and increases the level of oxygen.

D–C

- 'Clean air' is made up of 78% nitrogen, 21% oxygen and of the remaining 1%, only 0.035% is carbon dioxide.
- There's a balance between processes that use up carbon dioxide and make oxygen, and processes that use up oxygen and make carbon dioxide. These processes are shown in the **carbon cycle**.

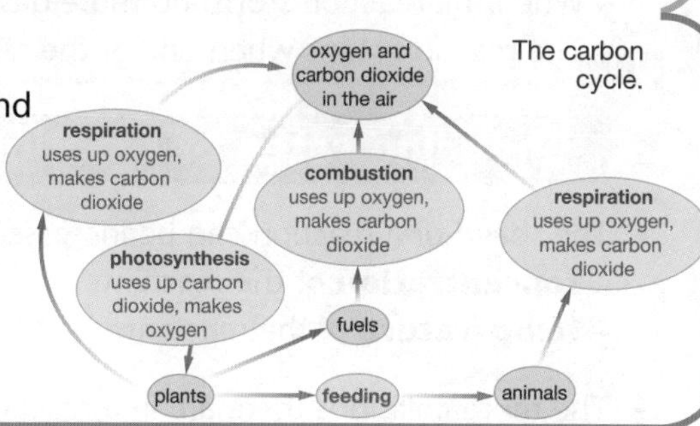

The carbon cycle.

The atmosphere

D–C

- Scientists **know** that gases trapped in liquid rock under the surface of the Earth are always escaping. This happens in volcanoes.
- Scientists **guess** about the original atmosphere of the Earth. It's known that at some point in the Earth's history, microbes developed that could photosynthesise. These organisms could remove carbon dioxide and add oxygen. Eventually the level of oxygen reached what it is today.

Pollution

G–E

- **Pollutants** are substances made by human activity that harm the environment. The atmosphere contains a large number of pollutants. The main ones are shown in the table.

pollutant	carbon monoxide	oxides of nitrogen	sulphur dioxide
environmental problem	a poisonous gas	photochemical smog and acid rain	acid rain kills plants and aquatic life, erodes stonework
origin of pollutant	incomplete combustion of petrol	formed in the internal combustion engine	sulphur impurities in fossil fuels

D–C

- **Atmospheric pollution** also affects people's health. The EU and the UK government have introduced many laws about pollution control, but still more controls are needed.
- A car fitted with a **catalytic converter** changes carbon monoxide into carbon dioxide. At the same time oxides of nitrogen are converted into nitrogen.

Questions

Grades G-E

1 What does combustion do to the levels of gases in the air?

Grades D-C

2 Which process in the carbon cycle uses up carbon dioxide?

Grades G-E

3 Which pollutant dissolves in water to produce acid which erodes statues?

Grades D-C

4 What does a catalytic converter do?

Faster or slower (1)

Grades

Rates of reaction

G–E

- A **chemical reaction** takes place when reactant **particles** hit or collide with each other.
- In a chemical reaction, **reactants** are made into **products**: reactants ⟶ products
- The **rate of reaction** measures how much product is made each second. Some reactions are very **fast** (**burning**) and others are very **slow** (**rusting**).
- If you measure the rate of reaction between magnesium and dilute hydrochloric acid, the **reaction time** is the time taken for all the magnesium to react.
  - The shorter the reaction time, the faster the reaction.
  - When the reaction stops, no more gas is made.
  - The reaction stops when one of the reactants is used up.

Changing rates of reaction

G–E

- The speed of a reaction can be increased by increasing the:
  - **concentration** of the reactants
  - **temperature** of the reactants
  - **pressure** of the reactants that are gases
  - **surface area** of the reactants.
- The more collisions there are in a reaction, the faster the reaction. The particles must be moving very fast and have lots of **kinetic energy** for collisions to occur.

D–C

The rate of a chemical reaction can be increased by increasing the **concentration**.

- As the concentration increases the particles become more crowded.
- Instead of four particles of **A**, there are ten particles of **A** in the same volume.
- The particles are more crowded, so there are more collisions and the rate of reaction increases.
- Graph A shows that a higher concentration of acid reacted with magnesium results in a quicker reaction rate, with the same amount of hydrogen collected. The gradient of the blue line is greater than the red line.

The rate of a chemical reaction can be increased by increasing the **temperature**.

- Particles move faster as the temperature increases.
- The reacting particles have more kinetic energy (shown by the thicker arrows) so the number of collisions increases and the rate of reaction increases.
- Graph B shows that in the same experiment between magnesium and acid a higher temperature results in a quicker reaction rate, with the same amount of hydrogen collected. The gradient of the blue line is greater than the red.

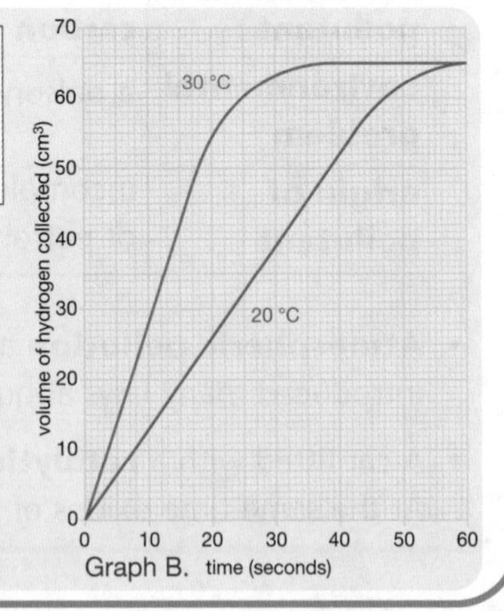

Graph B.

Questions

Grade G-E

1 Write down three ways that the rate of a reaction can be altered.

Grade D-C

2 Use ideas about particles to explain how the rate of a reaction can be altered.

3 How can the time taken for a reaction between magnesium and acid be measured?

4 If a reaction between the same mass of magnesium and excess acid is measured at two different temperatures, the total volume of gas produced doesn't change. Explain why.

Faster or slower (2)

Explosions

G–E

- An **explosion** happens when a reaction takes place very quickly. Explosions can include:
  - burning hydrogen
  - custard powder
  - TNT or dynamite.

D–C

- During an explosion, a large volume of gaseous products are released, moving outwards from the reaction at great speed causing the explosive effect.
- **Combustible powders** often cause explosions.
  - A powder reacts with oxygen to make large volumes of carbon dioxide and water vapour.
  - A factory using combustible powders such as sulphur, flour, custard powder or even wood dust must be very careful. The factory owners must ensure that the powders can't reach the open atmosphere and that the chance of producing a spark is very small.

Rates of reaction

G–E

- Powdered reactants always react faster than lumps.

D–C

- A powdered reactant has a much larger **surface area** than the same mass of a block of reactant.
- As the surface area of a solid reactant increases, so does the rate of reaction.

Fewer reacting particles of **B** can be in contact with reacting particles of **A**. As the surface area increases there are more collisions which means the rate of reaction increases.

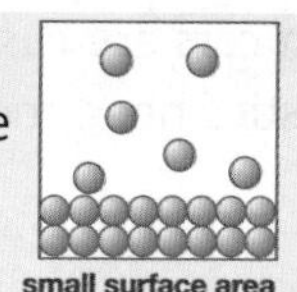

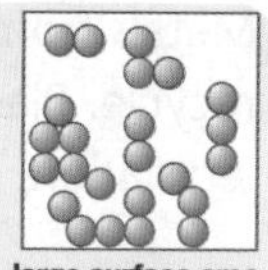

reacting particle of substance **A**
reacting particle of substance **B**

The graph shows how the rate of reaction between calcium carbonate and dilute hydrochloric acid is measured.

- As the reaction takes place, the mass on the balance (where the reacting substances are placed) decreases. This is because carbon dioxide gas is escaping.

  $CaCO_3 + 2HCl \longrightarrow CaCl_2 + H_2O + CO_2$
- The **gradient** of the graph is a measure of the rate of reaction. As the reaction takes place, the rate of reaction becomes less and less because the concentration of acid and the mass of calcium carbonate decrease.
- As the reaction proceeds there are fewer collisions between reactants.

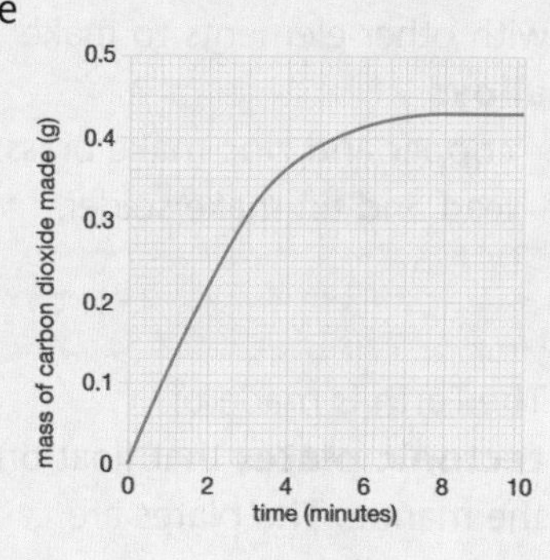

Catalysts

G–E

- A **catalyst** is a substance added to a chemical reaction to make the reaction go faster.

D–C

- A catalyst:
  - increases the rate of a reaction
  - is unchanged at the end of a reaction
  - is needed in small quantities to catalyse a large mass of reactants.

Questions

Grades D-C

1 Give two examples of combustible powders.

Grades G-E

2 Which reacts faster: powdered reactants or lumps of a reactant?

Grades D-C

3 Why is only 50 cm³ of hydrogen gas produced when using a 0.135 g lump of zinc with acid, compared to 100 cm³ of gas produced when using a 0.27 g lump of zinc?

Grades G-E

4 What's a catalyst?

C2 Summary

Paints and pigments

Paints are made from:
- **coloured rock** (pigment) particles
- **solvent**
- **binding medium**.

Paint is a **colloid**. It dries when the solvent evaporates.

Thermochromic pigments change colour on heating. **Phosphorescent pigments** glow in the dark. They store energy and release it as light over time.

Building materials

Building materials come from the ground. We use them directly or we turn the rock into concrete, glass and brick. Sand is turned into glass.

Huge amounts of **limestone** are quarried to make cement. Limestone is heated to thermally decompose it.

Metals

Metals from cars are easy to recycle. Plastics need more legislation.

Iron and aluminium are used in cars. Iron rusts, but aluminium doesn't. Iron is more dense than aluminium.

Pure metals can be mixed with other elements to make **alloys**.
- copper and zinc make brass
- lead and tin make solder.

Metals are extracted from metal ores. When they corrode, they change into oxides again.

Rusting is the chemical reaction between iron, oxygen and water. Acid rain accelerates this.

Earth and atmosphere

The Earth is made of **tectonic plates** that float on the mantle. The plates are moving all the time.

Moving tectonic plates trigger volcanic eruptions.

If molten rock cools slowly the crystals that are formed are bigger.

The atmosphere used to be poisonous, but plants produced oxygen. The composition of the atmosphere is now 21% oxygen and 78% nitrogen.

Carbon dioxide is given out in **combustion** but taken in during **photosynthesis**.

The Earth's original atmosphere came from gases escaping from the interior of the Earth.

Fast or slow?

Rates of reaction are affected by:
- **temperature**
- **surface area**
- **concentration**
- **catalysts**.

Explosions are chemical reactions that happen very quickly.

The higher the temperature, the faster the particles move. This increases the rate of reaction.

Grades

What are atoms like?

Atoms

G–E

- An **atom** is a **nucleus** surrounded by **electrons**.
  – The **nucleus** carries a **positive charge**.
  – The **electrons** carry a **negative charge**.

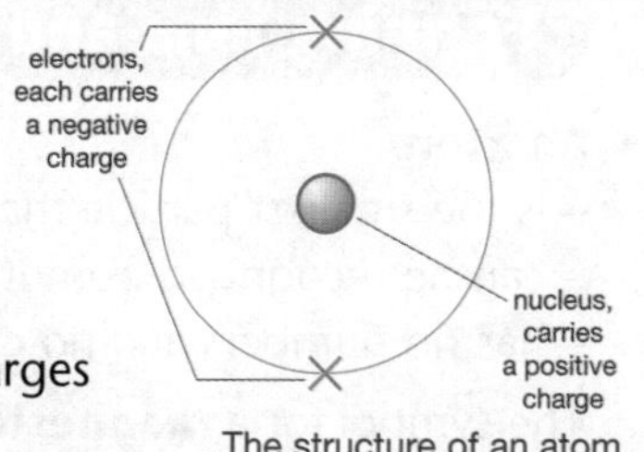

The structure of an atom.

- An atom is **neutral** because it has the same number of positive charges in the nucleus as there are negatively charged electrons around it.

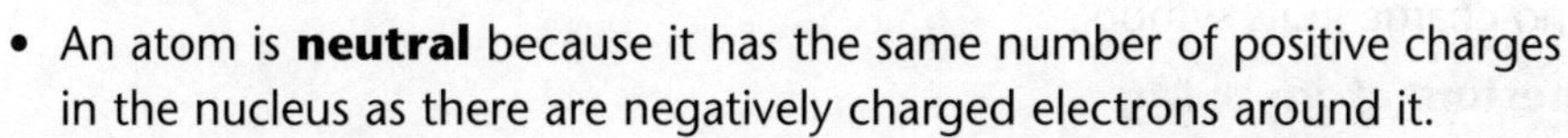

D–C

- The nucleus of an atom is made up of **protons** and **neutrons**.
- The **atomic number** is the number of protons in an atom.
- The **mass number** is the total number of protons and neutrons in an atom.

	relative charge	relative mass
electron	–1	0.0005 (zero)
proton	+1	1
neutron	0	1

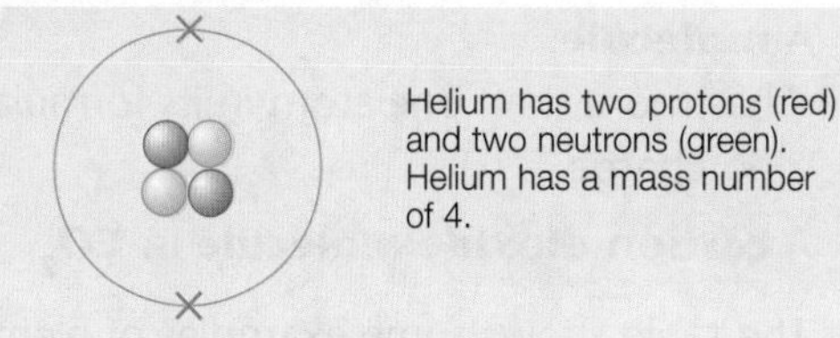

- The same number of electrons occupies the space around the protons of the nucleus.
- Electrons occupy **shells**. The electron shell nearest to the nucleus takes up to 2 electrons. The second shell takes up to 8 electrons.

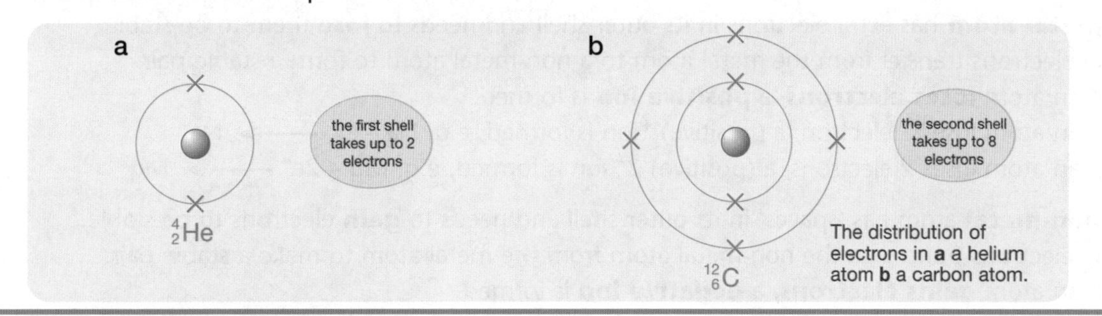

The distribution of electrons in **a** a helium atom **b** a carbon atom.

The periodic table

G–E

- Each atom has an **atomic number**. This number is written next to the **symbol** of an element in the **periodic table**. If the atomic number of an element is known, it can be identified by looking on the periodic table.

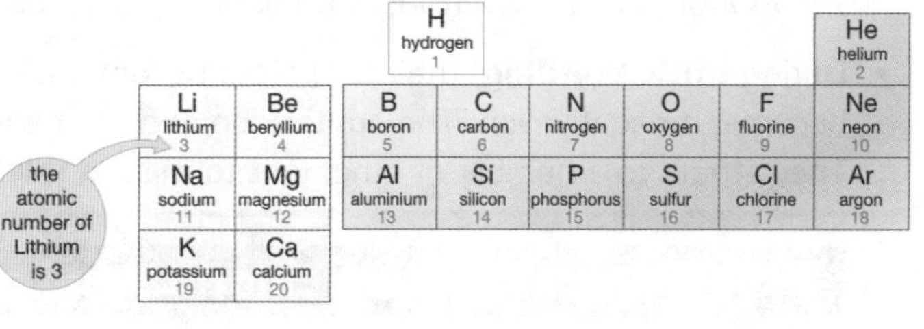

- An **element** is a substance that can't be broken down chemically. There are just over 100 **elements** in the **periodic table**. An element contains the same type of atom.

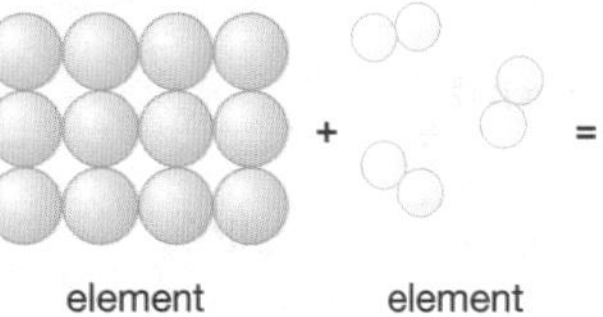

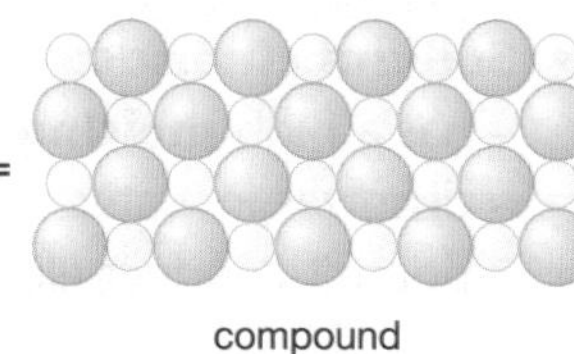

- A **compound** is a substance that contains at least two elements that are chemically joined together.

D–C

- The elements in the periodic table are arranged in **ascending** atomic number.
- **Isotopes** are elements that have the same atomic number but different mass numbers.

Questions

Grades G-E

1 What's the charge on a proton?

Grades D-C

2 What's the mass of one proton?

3 How many electrons does an atom of sodium have?

Grades G-E

4 Write down the names of the elements in copper sulphide.

Ionic bonding

Grades

Forming ions and molecules

G–E

- An **atom**:
  - is the smallest particle that can bond with another particle
  - can be recognised from its symbol, which has one capital letter and usually one lower case letter
  - has no numbers and no charge in its symbol.

The symbol for a **magnesium atom** is: **Mg**

- An **ion**:
  - is a **charged atom** or **group of atoms**
  - has a positive or negative charge on it.

A **calcium ion** has two positive charges: $\mathbf{Ca^{2+}}$

- A **molecule**:
  - has more than one atom in its formula and no charge.

A **carbon dioxide molecule** is: $\mathbf{CO_2}$

Atom	**Ion**	**Molecule**
H	H^+	H_2
O	O^{2-}	H_2O
Mg	Mg^{2+}	MgO
Cl	Cl^-	$MgCl_2$
Na	Na^+	NaOH
S	SO_4^{2-}	$MgSO_4$

- The table shows some examples of elements as atoms, ions and molecules.

Ionic bonding

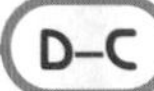

- A **metal atom** has extra electrons in its outer shell and needs to **lose** them to be stable. The electrons transfer from the metal atom to a non-metal atom to form a stable pair.
  - If an atom **loses electrons**, a **positive ion** is formed.
  - If an atom loses 1 electron, a (positive) $^+$ion is formed, e.g. $Na - e^- \longrightarrow Na^+$
  - If an atom loses 2 electrons, a (positive) 2^+ ion is formed, e.g. $Mg - 2e^- \longrightarrow Mg^{2+}$
- A **non-metal** atom has 'spaces' in its outer shell and needs to **gain** electrons to be stable. The electrons transfer to the non-metal atom from the metal atom to make a stable pair.
  - If an atom **gains electrons**, a **negative ion** is formed.
  - If an atom gains 1 electron, a (negative) $^-$ion is formed, e.g. $F + e^- \longrightarrow F^-$
  - If an atom gains 2 electrons, a (negative) 2^- ion is formed, e.g. $O + 2e^- \longrightarrow O^{2-}$
- During **ionic bonding**, the metal atom becomes a positive ion and the non-metal atom becomes a negative ion. The positive ion and the negative ion then attract one another. They attract to a number of other ions to make a solid **lattice**.

Properties of sodium chloride and magnesium oxide

G–E

- **Sodium chloride**:
  - has a high **melting point**
  - dissolves in water
  - doesn't conduct electricity when solid.
- **Magnesium oxide**:
  - has a very high melting point
  - doesn't conduct electricity when solid.

D–C

- Sodium chloride **solution** conducts electricity.
- **Molten** (melted) magnesium oxide and sodium chloride conduct electricity.

Questions

Grades G-E

1 Is Mg^{2+} an atom, a molecule or an ion?

Grades D-C

2 Explain how a negative ion is made from a neutral atom.

3 Explain the difference between how a metal atom and a non-metal atom transfer electrons.

Grades G-E

4 Describe the melting point of magnesium oxide.

Covalent bonding

Molecules

G–E

- A **molecule** forms when two or more non-metal **atoms** bond together.
- If a molecule has the formula $\mathbf{O_2}$, it has two oxygen atoms in its **molecular formula**, so the total number of atoms is two.

  Displayed formula: O═O Model:

- If a molecule has the formula $\mathbf{CO_2}$, it has one carbon atom and two oxygen atoms in its molecular formula, so the total number of atoms is three.

  Displayed formula: O═C═O Model:

Covalent bonding

G–E

- There are two types of bonding:
  - **ionic bonding** leads to large crystals
  - **covalent bonding** leads to molecules; examples are carbon dioxide (gas) and water (liquid), which have low melting points.

D–C

- Non-metals combine together by sharing **electrons**. This is called **covalent bonding**.

A molecule of **water** is made up of three atoms: two hydrogen and one oxygen.
- Oxygen has six electrons in its outer shell; it needs two more electrons to be complete.
- Hydrogen atoms each have one electron in their only shell, so the oxygen outer shell is shared with each of the hydrogen electrons.
- Now each of the hydrogen atoms has a share of two more electrons making the shell full.

A molecule of **carbon dioxide** is made up of three atoms: two oxygen and one carbon.
- Carbon has four electrons in its outer shell; it needs four more electrons to be complete.
- Oxygen atoms each have six electrons in their outer shell, so they each need two more electrons to be complete.
- The oxygen outer shell is shared with two of the electrons of the carbon outer shell each.
- Now each of the oxygen atoms has a share of two more electrons making the shell full.

- Carbon dioxide and water don't conduct electricity because they're covalently bonded.

The periodic table

G–E

- Look at part of the periodic table, right.
  - elements in the same **group** are in the same vertical **column**. They have similar **chemical properties**.
  - elements in the same **period** are in the same horizontal **row**.

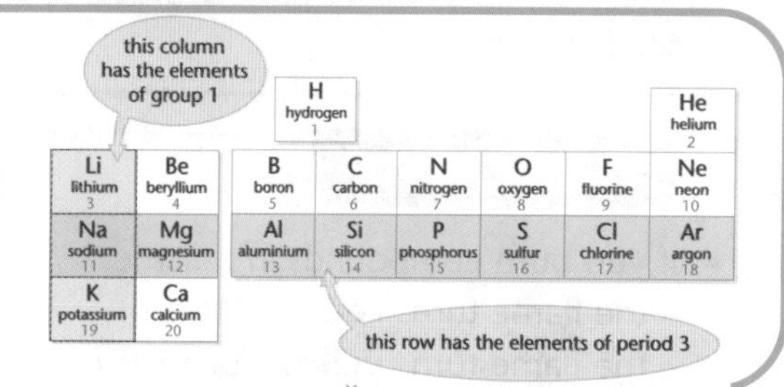

D–C

- This is how to tell which **group number** an element belongs to:
  - group 1 elements have 1 electron in the outer shell
  - group 7 elements have 7 electrons in the outer shell
  - group 8 elements have 8 electrons in the outer shell.

Group 1 Group 7 Group 8

- This is how to tell which **period** an element belongs to:
  - electrons in only **one shell**, it's in the **first period**
  - electrons in **two shells**, it's in the **second period**
  - electrons in **three shells**, it's in the **third period**.

element	electron	period
H	1	1
Li	2,1	2
Na	2, 8, 1	3

Questions

Grades G-E

1 How many different types of atom are there in a molecule of KNO_3?

Grades D-C

2 Draw a model showing the bonding of a water molecule.

Grades G-E

3 Name two elements in group 7.

Grades D-C

4 Sulphur has an electron pattern of 2, 8, 6. To which period does it belong?

The group 1 elements

Grades

Alkali metals

G–E

- Group 1 metals are called the **alkali metals**.
  - Alkali metals are stored under oil because they react with air and water.
  - Alkali metals react vigorously with water.
- The order of **reactivity** of the alkali metals with water is:
  - sodium is more reactive than lithium
  - potassium is more reactive than sodium.

lithium, sodium and potassium are metals in group 1

		H hydrogen 1					He helium 2
Li lithium 3	Be beryllium 4	B boron 5	C carbon 6	N nitrogen 7	O oxygen 8	F fluorine 9	Ne neon 10
Na sodium 11	Mg magnesium 12	Al aluminium 13	Si silicon 14	P phosphorus 15	S sulfur 16	Cl chlorine 17	Ar argon 18
K potassium 19	Ca calcium 20						

D–C

- When lithium, sodium and potassium react with water:
  - they float on the surface because their **density** is less than the density of water
  - hydrogen gas is given off
  - the metal reacts with water to form an **alkali** – the **hydroxide** of the metal.

Lithium reacts quickly and vigorously with water.
lithium + water ⟶ lithium hydroxide + hydrogen

Sodium reacts very quickly and vigorously with water and forms sodium hydroxide.
sodium + water ⟶ sodium hydroxide + hydrogen

Potassium reacts extremely vigorously with water and produces a lilac flame and forms potassium hydroxide.
potassium + water ⟶ potassium hydroxide + hydrogen

- Reactivity of the alkali metals with water increases down group 1.

reactivity increases down the group

	melting point in °C	boiling point in °C
$_3$Li	179	1317
$_{11}$Na	98	892
$_{19}$K	64	774

- These group 1 metals have **1 electron** in their **outer shell**. This is why group 1 metals have similar properties.

Flame tests

G–E

- If you burn compounds in a flame:
  - the flame turns **red** for **lithium**
  - the flame turns **yellow** for **sodium**
  - the flame turns **lilac** for **potassium**.

- If you want to test the flame colours of the chemicals:
  - put on safety goggles; moisten a flame test wire with dilute hydrochloric acid
  - dip the flame test wire into the sample of solid chemical
  - hold the flame test wire in a blue Bunsen burner flame
  - record the colour of the flame in a table.

Questions

Grades G-E
1 Why are group 1 metals kept under oil?

Grades D-C
2 Why does potassium float on water?

3 Explain why group 1 metals have similar properties.

Grades G-E
4 Which alkali metal compound produces a lilac flame?

Grades

The group 7 elements

The halogens

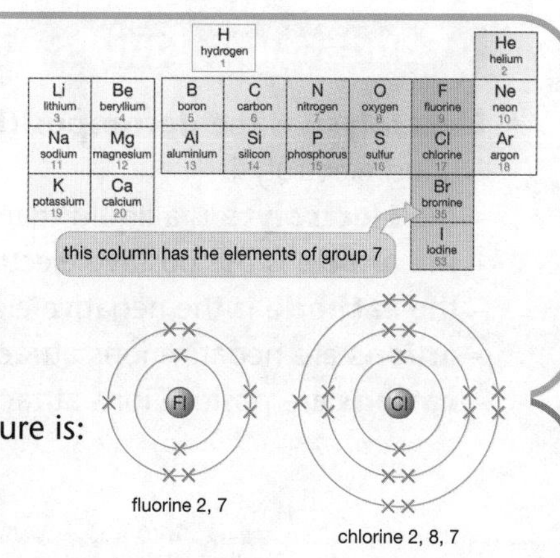

G–E

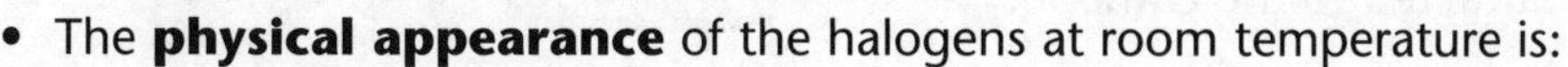

- Group 7 elements are called the **halogens** and include fluorine, chlorine, bromine and iodine. They have many uses:
  - **chlorine** is used to sterilise water
  - **iodine** is used to sterilise wounds
  - **sodium chloride** is used as a preservative, a flavouring and in the manufacture of chlorine.

D–C

- The **physical appearance** of the halogens at room temperature is:
  - chlorine is a green gas
  - bromine is an orange liquid
  - iodine is a grey solid.
- Group 7 elements have similar properties as they all have **7 electrons** in their **outer shell**.

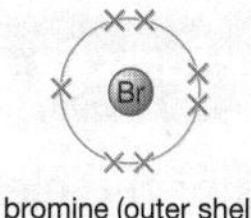

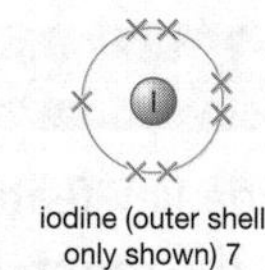

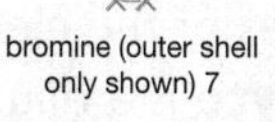

Halogens and reactivity

G–E

- There's a **trend** in the **reactivity** of halogens.
  - Fluorine is more reactive than chlorine.
  - Chlorine is more reactive than bromine.
  - Bromine is more reactive than iodine.
- Halogens react vigorously with **alkali metals**.

$_{9}F$
$_{17}Cl$
$_{35}Br$
$_{53}I$
reactivity

D–C

- When a halogen reacts with an alkali metal, a **metal halide** is made.

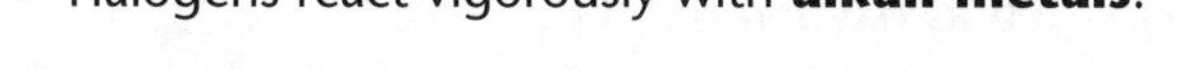

When lithium reacts with chlorine, the metal halide made is lithium chloride.
lithium + chlorine ⟶ lithium chloride

When potassium reacts with iodine, the metal halide made is potassium iodide.
potassium + iodine ⟶ potassium iodide

When sodium reacts with bromine, the metal halide made is sodium bromide.
sodium + bromine ⟶ sodium bromide

Displacement reactions of halogens

D–C

- The **reactivity** of the halogens decreases down the group.
- If halogens are bubbled through **solutions of metal halides**, there are two possibilities:
  - **no reaction**: if the halogen is less reactive than the halide in solution.
  - a **displacement reaction**: if the halogen is more reactive than the halide in solution.

Chlorine displaces the bromide to form bromine solution.
chlorine + potassium bromide ⟶ potassium chloride + bromine (orange solution)

Chlorine also displaces iodides from sodium iodide solution.
chlorine + sodium iodide ⟶ sodium chloride + iodine (red-brown solution)

Bromine displaces iodides from solutions.
bromine + potassium iodide ⟶ potassium bromide + iodine

Questions

Grades G-E

1 What are the elements of group 7 collectively known as?

2 Which element is more reactive: chlorine or iodine?

Grades D-C

3 Write down the word equation for the reaction between potassium and bromine.

4 Why does iodine *not* displace bromine from potassium bromide?

Electrolysis

Conducting liquids

G–E

- **Electrolysis** is the **decomposition** of a liquid using electricity. During electrolysis:
  - the **electrolyte** is a liquid that conducts electricity
  - the **anode** is the positive electrode
  - the **cathode** is the negative electrode
  - **anions** are negative ions attracted to the anode
  - **cations** are positive ions attracted to the cathode.

An electrolysis cell.

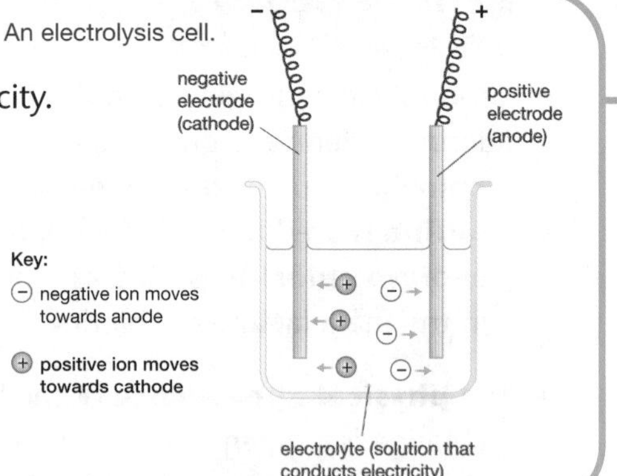

The electrolysis of dilute sulfuric acid

D–C

Electrolysis of sulphuric acid in the laboratory.

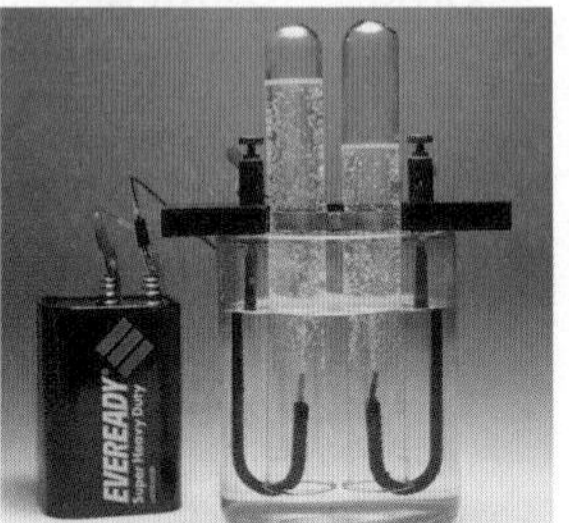

- The key features of the electrolysis of dilute sulfuric acid are:
  - the **electrolyte** is a dilute solution of sulfuric acid
  - two **electrodes** are connected to a DC supply, between 6 V and 12 V, and placed into the electrolyte
  - the electrode connected to the negative terminal is the **cathode**
  - the electrode connected to the positive terminal is the **anode**.
- When the current is switched on, bubbles of gas appear at both electrodes. Water splits into two ions: H^+ is the positive ion and OH^- is the negative ion.
  - H^+ is attracted to the negative cathode and discharged as hydrogen gas, H_2.
  - OH^- is attracted to the positive anode and discharged as oxygen gas, O_2.
- Twice the volume of hydrogen gas is given off as oxygen gas because the formula of the compound breaking up is H_2O.

Testing for hydrogen and oxygen

G–E

- Sulfuric acid solution can be broken down into hydrogen and oxygen.
- To test for the two gases: a lighted splint burns with a **'pop'** in **hydrogen**, a glowing splint **relights** in **oxygen**.

Electrolytic decomposition

- Aluminium is extracted from its **mineral** using electricity. The mineral is called **bauxite**.
- The key features in the production of aluminium by electrolytic decomposition are:
  - the use of molten aluminium oxide
  - aluminium is formed at the graphite cathode; oxygen is formed at the graphite anode
  - the anodes are gradually worn away by **oxidation**
  - the process requires a high electrical energy input.
- The word equation for the **decomposition of aluminium oxide** is:

  aluminium oxide ⟶ aluminium + oxygen

Questions

Grades G-E

1 Which electrode is the positive electrode?

Grades D-C

2 The ratio of hydrogen gas to oxygen gas made during the electrolysis of water is 2:1. Explain why.

Grades G-E

3 What's the mineral from which aluminium is extracted?

Grades D-C

4 What happens to the anodes during the process of electrolysis of aluminium?

Transition elements

Transition elements

G–E

- Transition elements are **metals** and have typical metallic properties. They:
  - conduct heat
  - are shiny
  - conduct electricity
  - are sonorous (ring when struck)
  - are malleable
  - are ductile.
- **Copper** and **iron** are examples of transition elements.

Key: relative atomic mass / atomic symbol / name / atomic (proton) number

1	2											3	4	5	6	7	8
			1 H hydrogen 1														4 He helium 2
7 Li lithium 3	9 Be beryllium 4											11 B boron 5	12 C carbon 6	14 N nitrogen 7	16 O oxygen 8	19 F fluorine 9	20 Ne neon 10
23 Na sodium 11	24 Mg magnesium 12											27 Al aluminium 13	28 Si silicon 14	31 P phosphorus 15	32 S sulfur 16	35.5 Cl chlorine 17	40 Ar argon 18
39 K potassium 19	40 Ca calcium 20	45 Sc scandium 21	48 Ti titanium 22	51 V vanadium 23	52 Cr chromium 24	55 Mn manganese 25	56 Fe iron 26	59 Co cobalt 27	59 Ni nickel 28	63.5 Cu copper 29	65 Zn zinc 30	70 Ga gallium 31	73 Ge germanium 32	75 As arsenic 33	79 Se selenium 34	80 Br bromine 35	84 Kr krypton 36
85 Rb rubidium 37	88 Sr strontium 38	89 Y yttrium 39	91 Zr zirconium 40	93 Nb niobium 41	96 Mo molybdenum 42	[98] Tc technetium 43	101 Ru ruthenium 44	103 Rh rhodium 45	106 Pd palladium 46	108 Ag silver 47	112 Cd cadmium 48	115 In indium 49	119 Sn tin 50	122 Sb antimony 51	128 Te tellurium 52	127 I iodine 53	131 Xe xenon 54
133 Cs caesium 55	137 Ba barium 56	139 La* lanthanum 57	178 Hf hafnium 72	181 Ta tantalum 73	184 W tungsten 74	186 Re rhenium 75	190 Os osmium 76	192 Ir iridium 77	195 Pt platinum 78	197 Au gold 79	201 Hg mercury 80	204 Tl thallium 81	207 Pb lead 82	209 Bi bismuth 83	[209] Po polonium 84	[210] At astatine 85	[222] Rn radon 86
[223] Fr francium 87	[226] Ra radium 88	[227] Ac* actinium 89	[261] Rf rutherfordium 104	[262] Db dubnium 105	[266] Sg seaborgium 106	[264] Bh bohrium 107	[277] Hs hassium 108	[268] Mt meitnerium 109	[271] Ds darmstadtium 110	[272] Rg roentgenium 111	Elements with atomic numbers 112±116 have been reported but not fully authenticated.						

The periodic table with the transition elements shaded in grey.

D–C

- A **compound** that contains a transition element is often coloured:
  - copper compounds are blue
  - iron(II) compounds are pale green
  - iron(III) compounds are orange/brown.
- A transition element and its compounds are often **catalysts**:
  - iron is used in the **Haber process** to make ammonia, which is used in fertilisers
  - nickel is used to harden the oils in the manufacture of margarine.

Top Tip!

A catalyst is an element or compound that changes the rate of a chemical reaction without taking part in the reaction. Catalysts are unchanged during the reaction.

Precipitation reaction

G–E

- **Precipitation** is a reaction between solutions that makes an **insoluble solid**.
  When a yellow solution of potassium chromate is added to a colourless solution of silver nitrate, a precipitate (solid) is formed. The **precipitate** is orange-coloured silver chromate.

Thermal decomposition

G–E

- **Thermal decomposition** is a reaction in which a substance is broken down into at least two other substances by heat.

D–C

- If a transition metal carbonate is heated, it **decomposes** to form a metal oxide and carbon dioxide. On heating:
  - $FeCO_3$ decomposes forming iron oxide and carbon dioxide
  - $CuCO_3$ decomposes forming copper oxide and carbon dioxide
  - $MnCO_3$ decomposes forming manganese oxide and carbon dioxide
  - $ZnCO_3$ decomposes forming zinc oxide and carbon dioxide.
- The metal carbonates change colour during decomposition.

Top Tip!

The test for carbon dioxide is that it turns limewater milky.

Sodium hydroxide solution

D–C

- Sodium hydroxide solution is used to identify the presence of transition metal ions in solution:
  - Cu^{2+} ions form a blue solid
  - Fe^{2+} ions form a grey/green solid
  - Fe^{3+} ions form an orange **gelatinous** solid.

Questions

Grades G-E

1 What are the symbols for copper and nickel?

Grades D-C

2 What colour are iron(III) compounds?

Grades G-E

3 What's a precipitation reaction?

Grades D-C

4 There's a difference between Fe^{2+} ions and Fe^{3+} ions. How would you show this using sodium hydroxide.

Metal structure and properties

Properties of metals

G–E

- Most metals:
  - are lustrous
  - are hard
  - have a high density
  - are good conductors of heat and electricity
  - have a high melting point and a high boiling point.
- The uses of a metal depend on its properties:
  - **Iron** is used to make **steel**. Steel is very strong and is used to make bridges.
  - **Copper** is used to make **brass**. Brass conducts electricity well and is used to make electrical wires.

D–C

- **Physical properties** of metals include:
  - having high thermal conductivity
  - being good conductors of heat
  - being malleable
  - being ductile
  - having high melting points and boiling points because of strong metallic bonds.

Copper is often used for the base or the whole of saucepans because it has high thermal conductivity.

- **Chemical properties** of metals include:
  - resistance to attack by oxygen or acids.

Copper is also resistant to chemicals, which is another reason why it's used for saucepans.

The structure of metals

G–E

- A metal is made of particles held together by **metallic bonds**.
- The particles in **solid metals** are:
  - close together
  - in a regular arrangement.
- A metal has a structure that contains crystals.

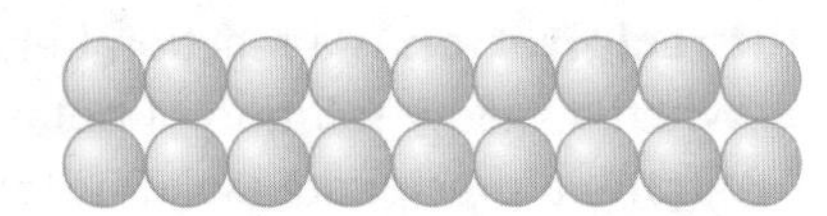

Metallic bonds hold the metal together.

Conductors and superconductors

G–E

- At very low temperatures some metals become **superconductors**.

- When metals conduct electricity, the electrons in the metal move. Superconductors are materials that conduct electricity with little or no resistance.
- When a substance goes from its normal state to a superconducting state, it no longer has any magnetic field. This is called the Meissner effect.
- The potential benefits of superconductors are:
  - loss-free power transmission
  - super-fast electronic circuits
  - powerful electromagnets.

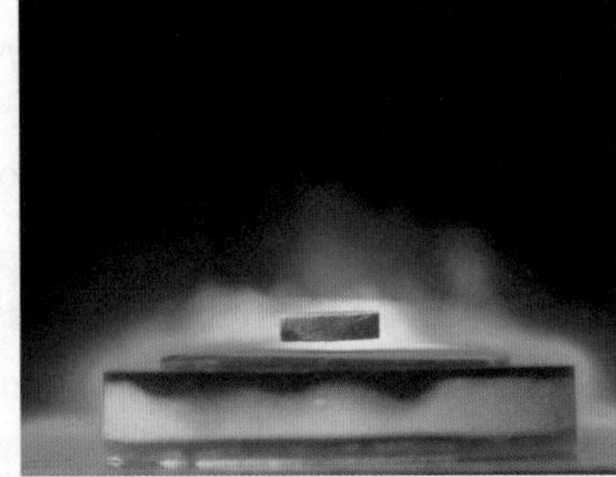

The permanent magnet levitates above the superconductor.

Questions

Grades G-E

1 Write down three properties of metals.

Grades D-C

2 Metals have high melting points. Explain why.

Grades G-E

3 What happens to some metals at very low temperatures?

Grades D-C

4 What happens if a small permanent magnet is put above a superconductor?

C3 Summary

Atoms and bonding

Atoms have a **positive nucleus** surrounded by **negative electrons**. The electrons are arranged in shells. The outer shell of electrons needs to be full to be **stable**.

Atoms **join together** to make **molecules** or large crystal structures. There are two ways in which atoms can bond, by **making ions** or by **sharing electrons**.

Ions are made when atoms **lose** or **gain electrons**. Ions are either positive or negative. If electrons are lost, a positive ion is made.

Atoms can share electrons to make molecules containing two or more atoms. This bonding is called **covalent bonding**.

Periodic table

Group 1 metals react vigorously with water to make alkaline solutions.

Group 7 elements are called the **halogens**. They have seven electrons in their outer shell.

The periodic table lists all elements in order of their **atomic number**.

The periodic table lists elements in **groups**. The elements have similar properties. They're in groups according to the pattern of their electrons.

Electrolysis

Pure water doesn't conduct electricity. If sulfuric acid is added, it decomposes to give hydrogen and oxygen gases.

Electrolysis is the decomposition of a substance using electricity.

Aluminium is made by the electrolysis of bauxite. The mineral has to be purified before it's used. The aluminium is deposited at the cathode.

Transition metals and metal structure

Iron, gold, silver, copper, nickel and chromium are all **transition metals**. They're used in a wide range of objects. Mercury is used in thermometers as it's a liquid metal at room temperature.

Metals **conduct electricity** easily because electrons move through the structure easily. At low temperatures some metals can become **superconductors**. These show little or no resistance when conducting electricity.

Transition metal compounds are usually coloured. The compounds often dissolve in water to make coloured solutions. The solutions react with sodium hydroxide to make **coloured precipitates**.

Acids and bases

Grades

Neutralising acids

G–E

- An acid can be **neutralised** by a **base** or **alkali**.
- **Sulphuric acid** can be used in:
  – the manufacture of fertilisers – cleaning metals – car battery acids.

D–C

- An alkali is a **base** which dissolves in water.
- The word equation for **neutralisation** is: acid + base ⟶ salt + water
- Metal oxides and metal hydroxides neutralise acids because they're bases. The reaction of a metal oxide or a metal hydroxide with an acid is:
  acid + oxide ⟶ salt + water acid + hydroxide ⟶ salt + water
- **Carbonates** also neutralise acids to give water and a gas:
  acid + carbonate ⟶ salt + water + carbon dioxide
- A **salt** is made from part of a base and part of an acid.
- To work out the name of a salt, look at the acid and base it was made from. The first part of the salt name is from the base and the second part from the acid.

Top Tip!

Nitrates come from nitric acid, chlorides come from hydrochloric acid, sulfates come from sulfuric acid.

When sodium hydroxide reacts with hydrochloric acid, the salt formed is sodium chloride:

sodium	**chloride**
from the base	from the acid

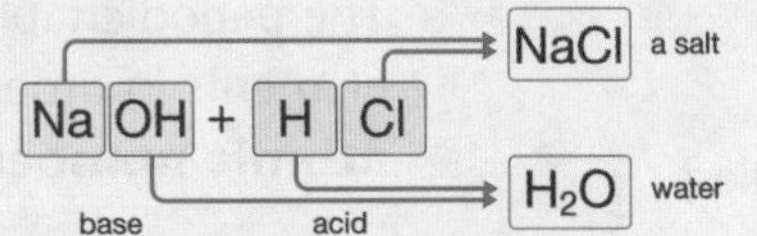

The pH scale

G–E

- The **pH scale** shows how acidic or alkaline a substance is.
  – A reading of pH = 1 shows a strong acid.
  – A reading of pH = 13 shows a strong alkali.

(low pH) **ACID** **pH = 0** acids have a pH of less than 7	**NEUTRAL** **pH = 7**	(high pH) **ALKALI** **pH = 14** Alkalis have a pH of more than 7

- The pH increases when an alkali is added and decreases when an acid is added.

D–C

- When an acid is added to alkali, or the other way round, a change in pH happens.

adding an alkali to an acid	**adding an acid to an alkali**
the pH at the start is low	the pH at the start is high
the pH rises as the alkali neutralises the acid	the pH falls as the acid neutralises the alkali
when neutral, the pH = 7	when neutral, the pH = 7
when more alkali is added, the pH rises above 7	when more acid is added, the pH falls below 7

- **Universal indicator solution** can be used to measure the acidity of a solution. A few drops are added to the test solution and then the colour of the solution is compared to a standard colour chart. When acid is added to alkali, they neutralise each other.

Colours for Universal indicator.

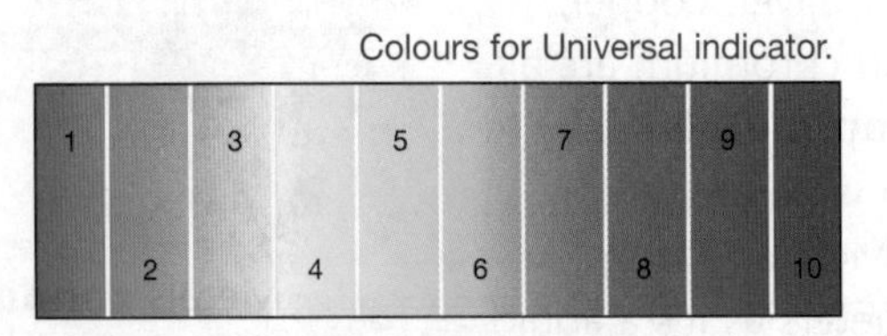

Questions

Grades G-E

1 Write down two uses of sulfuric acid.

Grades D-C

2 What's the base needed to make zinc sulfate?

Grades G-E

3 What's the pH of an acid?

Grades D-C

4 Which salt is made when magnesium hydroxide reacts with sulfuric acid?

Grades

Reacting masses

Relative atomic mass and relative formula mass

G–E

- Atoms of different elements 'weigh' different amounts. We compare their **masses** using the **relative atomic mass** scale. This can be found in the **periodic table**.
- If you add up all the masses in the formula of a compound you can work out the **relative formula mass** of the compound.

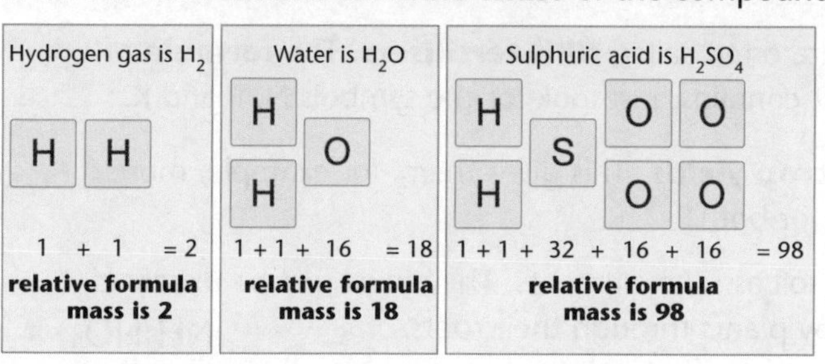

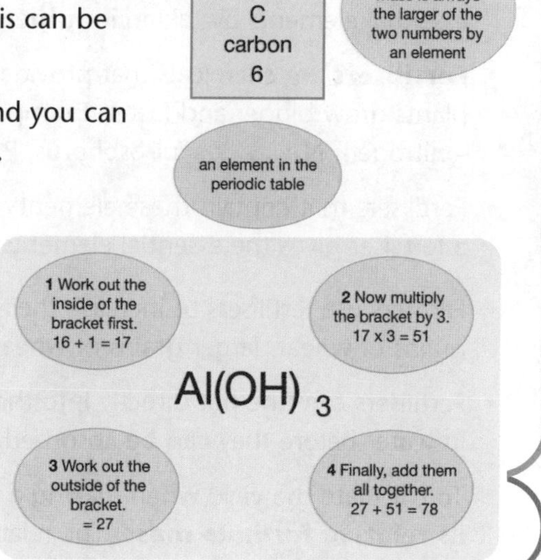

D–C

- Relative formula masses need to be added up in the right order if there are brackets in the formula.

Calculating mass and yield

G–E

- The total mass in a reaction never changes. The mass of the **products** (chemicals at the end) is exactly the same as the mass of the **reactants** (chemicals at the start).
- If the mass does seem to change, you need to look for a reason.
  – If the mass goes down, the reaction has given off a gas.
  – If the mass goes up, oxygen from the air has probably reacted with the chemical.
- The **yield** of a reaction is the amount of chemical that's produced in the reaction.
  – **100% yield** means that no product has been lost.
  – **0% yield** means that no product has been made.
- Sometimes a reaction doesn't give as much chemical as it should. Some chemicals always get left behind, so the amount of product that's collected is usually less than the amount that was expected. Some ways the product is lost include:
  – in **filtration** – small amounts stay on the filter paper
  – in **evaporation** – some chemicals evaporate into the room
  – in **transferring** liquids – tiny amounts of liquid stick to the sides of the beaker
  – because more than one reaction might be taking place, so the reactants are being used up in a different reaction.

D–C

- Calculations can be made of how much product is produced in a reaction without knowing the equations for the reactions.
- To calculate percentage yield, the following two things must be known:
  – the amount of product made, the 'actual yield'
  – the amount of product that should have been made, the 'predicted yield'.

$$\text{percentage yield} = \frac{\text{actual yield}}{\text{predicted yield}} \times 100$$

Questions

You may need to use the periodic table on page 4 to help you to answer the questions.

Grades G-E

1 Work out the relative formula mass of zinc carbonate, $ZnCO_3$.

Grades D-C

2 Write down the relative formula mass of calcium nitrate, $Ca(NO_3)_2$.

Grades G-E

3 Suggest two reasons why a yield is less than 100%.

Grades D-C

4 Tim made 24 g of crystals instead of 32 g. What's the percentage yield?

Fertilisers and crop yield

Fertilisers

G–E

- Carbon dioxide and water don't give a plant all the **elements** that it needs. It gets these essential elements by taking in **minerals** through its roots.
- **Fertilisers** are chemicals that provide plants with essential chemical elements to help plants grow bigger and faster. Examples are:
  – nitrogen, N – phosphorus, P – potassium, K.
- Fertilisers that contain these elements are often called **NPK fertilisers**. The **formula** of a fertiliser gives the essential elements it contains. Just look for the symbols N, P and K.

D–C

- Farmers use fertilisers to increase their **crop yields**. This gives them, for example, more grains of wheat, larger grains of wheat, or both.
- Fertilisers can't be put directly into the soil as pure elements. They must first be dissolved in water before they can be absorbed by plants through their roots.
- To calculate the yield when making a fertiliser, you need to calculate its **relative formula mass**. The relative formula mass of ammonium nitrate, NH_4NO_3, is 80.

NH_4NO_3

14 | 4 x 1 = 4 | 14 | 3 x 16 = 48

14 + 4 + 14 + 48 = 80

Making fertilisers

G–E

- Fertilisers can be made by **neutralising** alkalis with acids.

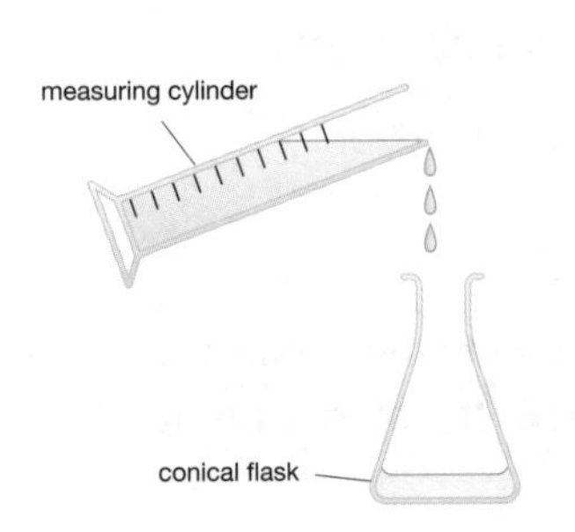

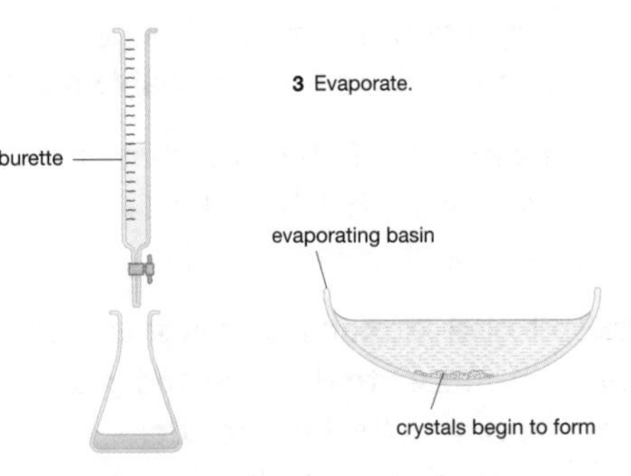

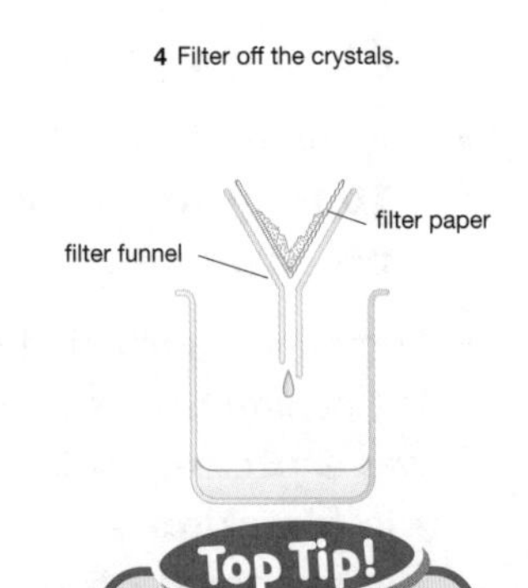

- A fertiliser that contains nitrogen is called a **nitrogenous** fertiliser. Some examples are:
  – ammonium nitrate – ammonium sulphate
  – ammonium phosphate – urea.

Top Tip!
These nitrogenous fertilisers are all manufactured from ammonia.

D–C

- Many fertilisers are **salts**, so they can be made by reacting acids with bases.
  acid + base ⟶ salt + water

nitric acid + potassium hydroxide ⟶ potassium nitrate + water
nitric acid + ammonium hydroxide ⟶ ammonium nitrate + water
sulphuric acid + ammonium hydroxide ⟶ ammonium sulphate + water
phosphoric acid + ammonium hydroxide ⟶ ammonium phosphate + water

Questions

Grades G-E

1 What are the essential elements in potassium phosphate, K_3PO_4?

Grades D-C

2 What's the relative formula mass of ammonium phosphate, $(NH_4)_3PO_4$?

Grades G-E

3 Write down two nitrogenous fertilisers.

Grades D-C

4 Which acid and base react to make potassium phosphate?

The Haber process

Ammonia

G–E

- Ammonia is made by joining **nitrogen** and **hydrogen** in the **Haber process**.
  – Nitrogen comes from air.
  – Hydrogen is made from natural gas or by **cracking** oil fractions.
- The Haber process has two reactions.

nitrogen + hydrogen ⟶ **ammonia** A forward reaction.

nitrogen + hydrogen ⟵ **ammonia** A backward reaction.

- The reaction goes in both directions – at the same time. Reactions that go in both directions are called **reversible reactions**.
- To write an equation for a reversible reaction a special arrow is used: $\rightleftharpoons$.

nitrogen + hydrogen $\rightleftharpoons$ ammonia

- Eighty per cent of all ammonia goes into fertilisers. Ammonia is also used to make nitric acid, most of which goes into more fertilisers. Some ammonia is used to make household cleaners.

The Haber process

D–C

- The Haber process uses:
  – an iron catalyst
  – high pressure
  – a temperature of 450 °C
  – a recycling system for unreacted nitrogen and hydrogen.

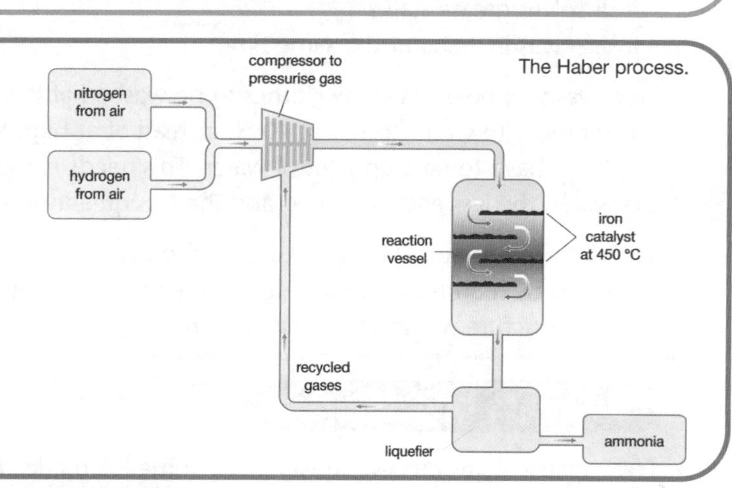

The Haber process.

The costs of ammonia production

G–E

- The cost of making the ammonia is affected by:
  – the cost of building the plant
  – people's wages
  – the cost of the raw materials
  – nitrogen and hydrogen and the energy costs
  – how quickly the new substance can be made (cost of a catalyst).

D–C

- Different factors affect the cost of making a new substance:
  – **labour** – chemical plants are heavily automated and need few people to operate them
  – **reactants** – hydrogen is made from natural gas or by cracking oil, which costs money; nitrogen has to be cleaned, dried and compressed
  – **recycling** of unreacted materials – means that money isn't wasted
  – **high pressure** – this makes the reaction work better but costs more
  – **energy** – the higher the temperature, the more fuel is needed
  – **reaction rate** – the faster the reaction, the more product is made from the same equipment, so the cheaper it is
  – **pollution control** – reducing pollution is expensive.

Questions

Grades G-E

1 What's ammonia made from?

Grades D-C

2 At what temperature is the Haber process carried out?

Grades G-E

3 Write down three costs of making ammonia.

Grades D-C

4 Why is low pressure not used in the Haber process?

Detergents

Grades

Washing powders

G–E

- A **detergent** is a salt. The ingredients in washing powders include:
  - **active detergent**, which does the cleaning
  - **water softener** to soften hard water
  - **bleaches** to remove coloured stains
  - **optical brighteners** to give a whiter than white appearance
  - **enzymes** to remove food stains at low temperatures.

perfume makes clothes smell nice
detergent lifts dirt off clothes
bleach 'removes' coloured stains
Automatic biological SUNSHINE soap powder 2.5kg 2.5kg
enzymes remove food stains, they only work at low temperatures
optical brightener sticks to clothes and makes them 'whiter than white'
water softener softens hard water

Some of the things in washing powder.

D–C

- A detergent can be made by **neutralising** an organic acid using an alkali.
  acid + alkali ⟶ salt + water
  It's suitable for cleaning uses because:
  - it dissolves grease stains
  - it dissolves in water at the same time.
- New washing powders allow clothes to be washed at low temperatures. It's good for the environment to wash clothes at 40 °C instead of at high temperatures because washing machines have to heat up a lot of water. This needs energy, so the lower the temperature of the water, the less energy is used and the less greenhouse gases are put into the atmosphere.
- Washing clothes at low temperatures is also good for coloured clothes as many dyes are easily damaged by high temperatures. It also means that many more fabrics can be machine washed as their structure would be damaged at higher temperatures.

Solvents and solutes

G–E

- Fresh coffee stains dissolve in water but some ink marks don't. However, some ink marks will often dissolve in methylated spirit.
  - Methylated spirit and water are both **solvents** – they dissolve other substances.
  - The substance that dissolves, the ink, is a **solute**.
  - Ink dissolved in a solvent makes a **solution**.
- Different solvents dissolve different substances. If a substance dissolves, it's **soluble**. If it doesn't dissolve, it's **insoluble**.

Dry cleaning

D–C

- Some fabrics will be damaged if they are washed in water, so they must be **dry-cleaned**. A dry-cleaning machine washes clothes in an organic solvent. The word 'dry' doesn't mean that no liquids are used, just that the liquid solvent isn't water.
- Most of the stains on clothing contain grease from the skin or from food. Grease-based stains won't dissolve in water, but they will dissolve easily in a dry-cleaning solvent.

Questions

Grades G-E

1 Why are enzymes used in washing powders?

Grades D-C

2 What are the two reactants used in making a detergent?

Grades G-E

3 What does a solute dissolve in to make a solution?

Grades D-C

4 Give two reasons why a dry-cleaning method may be used.

Batch or continuous?

Grades

Making chemicals

G–E

- If a chemical is needed in large amounts, it's usually made by a **continuous process**.
- A continuous process is one which doesn't stop and reactants are continually fed in.
- Ammonia is made by a continuous process.
- Speciality chemicals, such as medicines and pharmaceutical drugs, are often made on demand in a **batch process**.

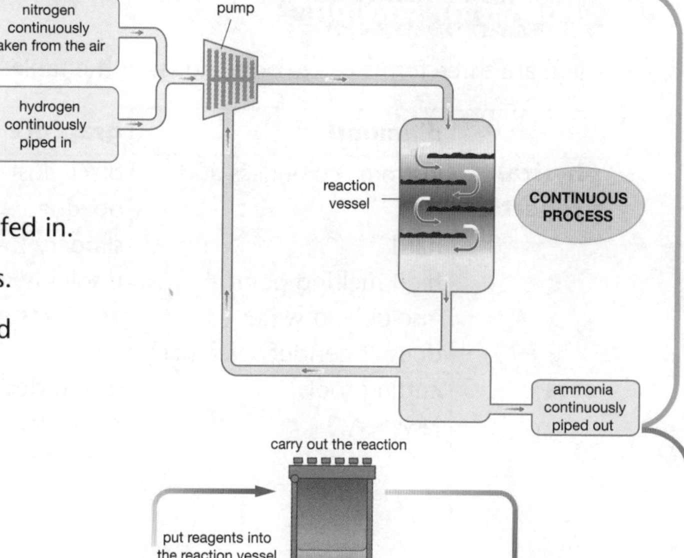

D–C

- Drugs companies make medicines in small batches, which are then stored.
  - New batches are made when the stored medicine runs low. If a lot of one medicine is needed, several batches can be made at the same time.
  - Once they have made a batch of one drug, it's easy to switch to making a different drug.
- The large scale production of ammonia is different to the small scale production of pharmaceuticals as it's a continuous process.

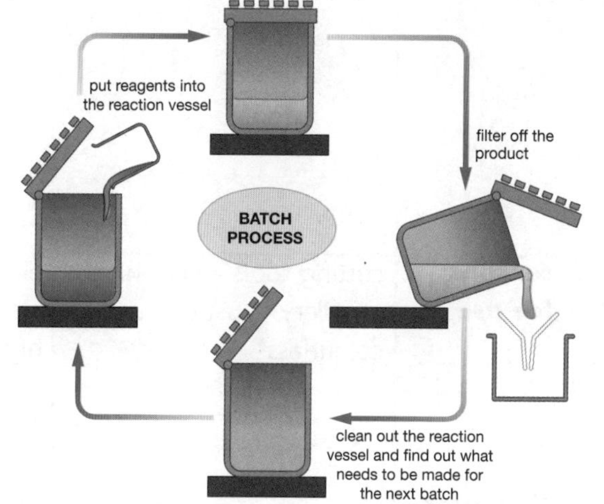

Raw materials

G–E

- The raw materials for a medicine can be made synthetically or extracted from plants.

D–C

- Chemical compounds in a plant are held in its cells. Plant cells have tough walls, so to extract the compound the plant is **crushed** to break the cell walls.
- Then the chemical must be **dissolved**. This only works if a suitable **solvent** is used.
- The solvent dissolves lots of different compounds, so the desired compound is then separated from the others. This can be done by **chromatography**.

Factors affecting the costs of medicines

G–E

- Factors affecting the cost of making and developing medicines and pharmaceutical drugs are shown here.

labour costs
research and testing
energy costs
DRUG COST
raw materials
time for development
marketing, legal costs

D–C

- The high costs of making and developing medicines and pharmaceutical drugs include:
  - **strict safety laws**
  - **research and development** – take years to develop
  - **raw materials** – may be rare and costly
  - **labour intensive** – because medicines are made by a batch process, less automation can be used.

Questions

Grades G-E

1 What's a continuous process?

Grades D-C

2 What's a batch process?

Grades G-E

3 Write down three costs involved in developing a medicine.

Grades D-C

4 Give two reasons why medicines are expensive to develop.

Nanochemistry

Grades

Forms of carbon

G–E

- There are three forms of **carbon** shown in the table.

	diamond	**graphite**	**buckminster fullerene**
physical properties	lustrous, colourless and clear hard high melting point insoluble in water doesn't conduct electricity	black, lustrous and opaque slippery insoluble in water conducts electricity	black solid deep red in solution in petrol
uses	cutting tools jewellery	electrodes pencil leads lubricants	can join together to make nanotubes that are very strong and can conduct electricity semiconductors in electrical circuits (nanotubes) industrial catalysts (nanotubes) reinforces graphite in tennis rackets (nanotubes)
reasons for use	cutting tools – very hard jewellery – lustrous and colourless	electrodes – conducts electricity and has high melting point pencil leads – slippery and black lubricants – slippery	
structure			

D–C

Nanochemistry

G–E

- Chemistry works with materials on a large scale.
- Nanochemistry works at the level of atoms – **nanoscale**.

D–C

- A **fullerene** changes at the **nanoscale**. The shape of the individual particles – balls or tubes, sieves or cages – is their nanostructure. This gives them their **nano properties**, which are different from **bulk properties**. Bulk chemical properties are the properties of large amounts of a material.

Questions

Grades G-E

1 Write down three different forms of carbon.

Grades D-C

2 Which properties of graphite make it useful as an electrode?

Grades G-E

3 What does 'nanochemistry' mean?

Grades D-C

4 What are bulk chemical properties?

Grades

How pure is our water?

Water

G–E

Water
Where water is found in the United Kingdom:
- lakes
- rivers
- aquifers
- reservoirs.

Water as a resource
Water is used by industry as:
- a cheap raw material
- a coolant
- a valuable solvent.

What's in water before it's purified?
- dissolved salts and minerals
- pollutants
- insoluble materials
- microbes (killed by chlorination).

Pollutants in drinking water
- nitrate residues
- lead compounds
- pesticide residues.

D–C

- Clean water saves more lives than medicines. That's why, after disasters and in developing countries, relief organisations concentrate on providing clean water supplies.
- Water is a **renewable resource**, but that doesn't mean the supply is endless. If there isn't enough rain in the winter, reservoirs don't fill up properly for the rest of the year.
- Producing tap water does incur costs. It takes energy to pump and to purify it – all of which increases climate change.

Water purification

D–C

- The water in a river is cloudy and often not fit to drink. It may also contain pollutants such as nitrates from fertiliser run off, lead compounds from lead pipes, and pesticides from spraying near to water resources. To make drinking water clean, it's passed through a **water purification** works.
- There are three main stages in water purification:
  - **sedimentation** of particles – larger bits drop to the bottom
  - **filtration** of very fine particles – sand is used to filter out finer particles
  - **chlorination** – kills microbes.

Precipitation reactions for testing water

G–E

- To test whether water contains sulfate or halide ions, we use a **precipitation reaction**.
- To test for **sulfate ions**, we add two drops of **barium chloride** solution to the water:
  - **sulfates** give a **white** precipitate
- To test for **chloride**, **bromide** and **iodide ions**, we add one or two drops of **silver nitrate** solution to the water in the test tube:
  - **chlorides** give a white precipitate
  - **bromides** give a cream precipitate
  - **iodides** give a yellow precipitate.

D–C

- In a precipitation reaction, two solutions react to form a solid that doesn't dissolve.

lead nitrate + sodium **sulfate** ⟶ lead sulphate (**white** precipitate) + sodium nitrate
silver nitrate + sodium **chloride** ⟶ silver chloride (**white** precipitate) + sodium nitrate
silver nitrate + sodium **bromide** ⟶ silver bromide (**cream** precipitate) + sodium nitrate
silver nitrate + sodium **iodide** ⟶ silver iodide (**yellow** precipitate) + sodium nitrate

Questions

Grades G-E

1 Write down three places that we get water from.

Grades D-C

2 Explain why filtration is used in the water purification process.

Grades G-E

3 What type of reaction takes place between barium chloride and sulfates?

4 What chemical is added to water to test for bromide ions?

C4 Summary

Chemical industry

Ammonia is made all the time in a **continuous process**. Pharmaceutical drugs are made on a smaller scale by a **batch process**.

Nitrogen and hydrogen make ammonia in the **Haber process**.

We can change the **conditions** in the Haber process to give us the best **yield**.

Ammonia reacts as a **base** to form fertilisers such as ammonium nitrate and ammonium phosphate.

If we know the mass of the reactants, we can work out what mass of products to expect.

Industry makes chemicals such as **fertilisers**. They must be cheap enough to use.

We can measure the **percentage yield** of a reaction.

$$\% \text{ yield} = \frac{\text{actual yield}}{\text{predicted yield}} \times 100$$

Different factors affect the **cost** of making new fertilisers or any new substance. High pressures mean higher energy costs.

Fertilisers make crops grow bigger as they provide plants with extra nitrogen, phosphorus and potassium. These are essential chemical elements for plant growth.

Water resources are found in lakes, rivers, aquifers and reservoirs.
Water needs testing and purifying before use.
Purification includes:
- filtration
- sedimentation
- chlorination.

Detergents do the active cleaning in washing up liquid and washing powder. Detergents are molecules that combine with both grease and water. Washing powders have optical brighteners added to make clothes look whiter than white.

Nanochemistry

Diamonds are used in cutting tools and jewellery. They're **very hard** and have a **high melting point**.

Graphite is carbon. It's **slippery** so it can be used as a lubricant. It also **conducts electricity** so it can be used as electrodes.

The element carbon can exist in different forms. This is due to differences at the **nanoscale**.

Fullerenes were discovered fairly recently.
Buckminster fullerene has the formula C_{60}.

Moles and empirical formulae

The mole

G–E

- The **mole** is a scientist's name for a standard amount of particles.
- A mole of anything always contains the same number of particles. This number is very, very big.
- Lots of things come in standard amounts with special names such as pair (2), a dozen (12), a mole (a huge number!).

Each dish has one mole of a different compound. They do not have the same mass but they do all contain the same amount of particles.

Relative atomic mass, relative formula mass and molar mass

G–E

- On page 33 you learned about **relative atomic mass** and **relative formula mass**.

What is the relative formula mass of carbon dioxide, CO_2?

Relative atomic masses C = 12, O = 16

Relative formula mass is (12 + 16 + 16) = 44

- The mass of one mole of a substance is called its **molar mass**.
- The molar mass is the relative formula mass of a substance in grams.

substance	relative formula mass	molar mass
H atoms	1	1 g
H_2 molecules	2	2 g
O atoms	16	16 g
O_2 molecules	32	32 g
H_2O molecules	18	18 g
C atoms	12	12 g
CO_2 molecules	44	44 g

The molar mass of water is 18 g. This is because the formula is H_2O.

The relative atomic mass of H is 1 and of O is 16.

D–C

The molar mass of ammonium sulfate, $NH_4(SO_4)_2$ is 14 + (4 × 1) + 2(32 + 64) = 210 g.

The relative atomic masses are: H = 1, O = 16, N = 14, S = 32.

Empirical formula

D–C

- The **empirical formula** is the ratio of each type of atom present in a compound.
- An empirical formula must be a whole number ratio.

The empirical formula of heptene, C_7H_{14} is the ratio of the atoms C and H – CH_2.

- The empirical formula for glucose ($C_6H_{12}O_6$) and ethanoic acid (CH_3COOH) is the same – CH_2O – yet the two compounds are very different.

Questions

Grades G-E

1 What is the relative formula mass of ethane, C_2H_6?

Grades D-C

2 What is the molar mass of this acid: $CH_3C(CH_3)_2COOH$?

Grades G-E

3 What is the molar mass of methanoic acid, HCOOH?

Grades D-C

4 What is the empirical formula for hexane, C_6H_{14}?

Electrolysis

Grades

Decomposing electrolytes

G–E

- An **electrolyte** is a liquid compound which breaks down when electricity is passed through it.
- An electrolyte is made into a liquid by melting it or dissolving it in water.
- Electrolytes are made of ions. They break up when the current flows.

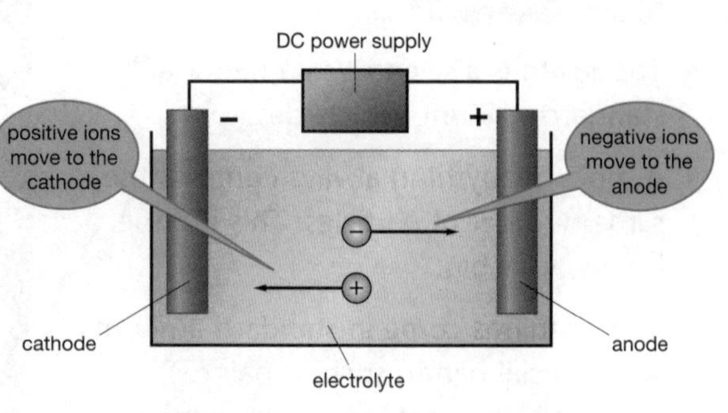

- At the **cathode** (negative electrode) positive ions are discharged.

electrolyte	at cathode	at anode
potassium chloride KCl	potassium	chlorine
lead iodide PbI_2	lead	iodine
aluminium oxide Al_2O_3	aluminium	oxygen

- At the **anode** (positive electrode) negative ions are discharged.

D–C

- Electric current is a flow of charge.
- Electrolytes are ionic. The charge moves through the electrolyte by the **ions** moving.
- If the electrolyte solidifies then the ions cannot move and the **current** cannot flow.
- Positive ions move toward the cathode. Negative ions move toward the anode.
- Ions reach the electrodes and are discharged; they turn into atoms or molecules.
- If the electrolyte is a solution, water is present as well. Hydrogen is made at the cathode and oxygen at the anode. For example: potassium nitrate solution, KNO_3(aq).

What affects the amount produced?

G–E

- Two things have an effect on electrolysis reactions: size of current and time.
- The electrolysis of copper(II) sulfate using copper electrodes is a special case:
  - the electrolyte is a solution, not a melted compound
  - the electrodes themselves take part in the electrolysis.

at the negative cathode	at the positive anode
copper sticks onto cathode, cathode becomes copper plated	copper leaves anode, anode dissolves

D–C

- The amount produced at each electrode increases with increased current and with time.
- Discharged ions are produced at the electrodes.
- The number of ions discharged is affected by the amount of charge transferred.
- The electrolysis of copper(II) sulfate using copper electrodes is a different reaction:
  - the cathode gets heavier as it is plated
  - the anode gets lighter as it dissolves
  - each electrode changes by the same amount.

Questions

Grades G-E

1 When molten lead iodide is electrolysed, which ions are discharged?

Grades D-C

2 Which type of ions move towards the cathode during electrolysis?

Grades G-E

3 What happens to the anode when copper sulfate is electrolysed with copper electrodes?

Grades D-C

4 Write down two quantities that change the amount produced at an electrode.

Quantitative analysis

Recommended daily allowances [RDA]

G–E

- Breakfast cereals show **recommended daily allowances** for vitamins and minerals.
- Packaged foods often have suggested daily amounts for some of the contents.
- For sodium, this is 2 g for women and 2.8 g for men.
- If it is written as 'salt' then it is 5 g and 7 g.
- Packaged food has a lot of salt.

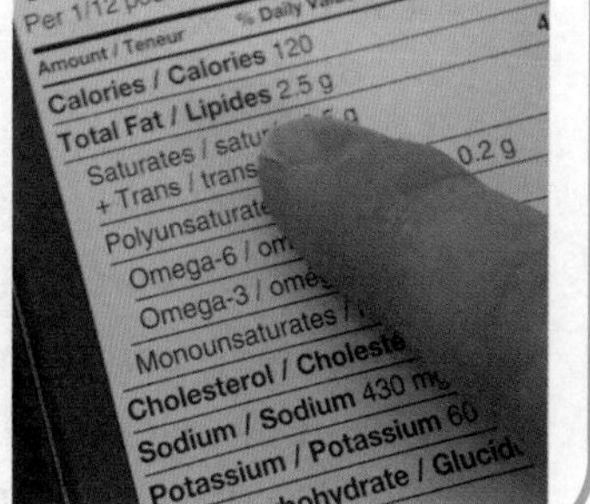
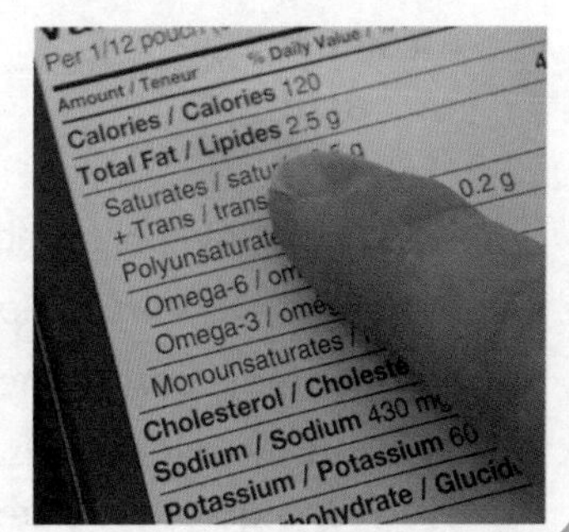

Solutes and solutions

D–C

- The substance dissolved in a liquid is the **solute**.
- The more concentrated the solution, the more crowded the solute particles.
- The more dilute, the less crowded the solute particles.

Solutions and concentration

G–E

- Concentration is the amount dissolved in 1 dm^3 of solution.
- Mass dissolved is measured in g/dm^3 (g per dm^3).
- Moles dissolved is measured in mol/dm^3 (mol per dm^3).
- Concentration is important. Sachets of baby milk must be mixed with the right amount of water.
  – If the balance is right the baby can take all it needs.
  – Too much water and the baby won't get enough food.
  – Too much powder causes digestive problems for the baby.
- You can't always use the same amounts. For example, windscreen wash fluid is added to water. In winter the solution must be more concentrated to stop the water freezing.

How to dilute solutions

D–C

- If a solution is three times more dilute, it takes up three times more volume.

You have to make a solution 10 times more dilute.

You start with 1 cm^3.

Starting volume is 1 cm^3, final volume is 10 cm^3.

Extra to be added $10 - 1 = 9$ cm^3 of water.

Questions

Grades G-E

1 What is a 'recommended daily allowance'?

Grades D-C

2 What is a 'solute'?

Grades G-E

3 Why is it important to dilute some liquids such as orange squash?

Grades D-C

4 You have a 10 cm^3 of a solution. You want to make it 10 times as dilute. How much water do you add to it?

Titrations

Grades

Changing pH

G–E

low pH acid		neutral		high pH alkali
0	←	7	→	14

- **Acids** have low pH numbers. **Alkalis** have high pH numbers.
- Adding acid **lowers** the pH. Adding alkali **increases** the pH.
- A pH meter is best at measuring pH.
- Universal indicator (UI) solutions and paper are good for a quick estimate of pH by comparing the colour of the solution with a reference card.

Colours for Universal indicator.

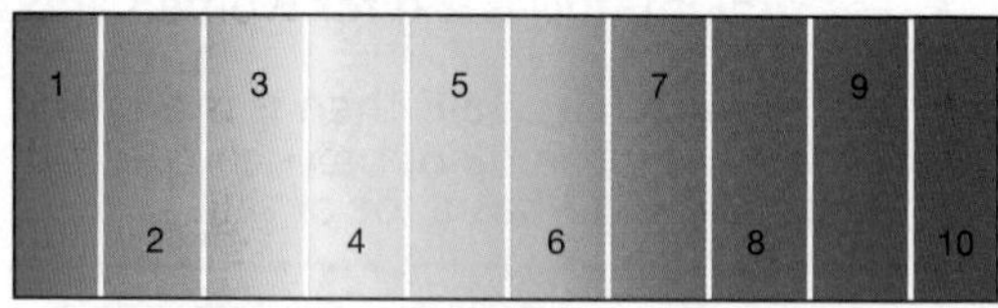

D–C

- When an acid reacts with an alkali, the pH of the solution changes.
- At the start when there is just alkali, the pH number is high.
- As the acid starts to **neutralise** the alkali, the pH falls.
- A salt is made:

  acid + alkali ⟶ salt + water
- The point where the acid has just reacted with all the alkali is the **end point**.
- At the end point the pH changes very suddenly.

Indicators

G–E

- Some jobs in the laboratory can be automated. Titrations are often carried out by hand.

  1 Use a pipette filler to **pipette** a volume of alkali into the conical flask.

  2 Put a few drops of **indicator** into the flask.

  3 Add the acid from a **burette** slowly to the alkali.

  4 Stop when the indicator suddenly changes colour – this is the **end point**.

  5 Repeat stages 1–5 until the readings agree.
- UI shows a range of colours through the pH range.
- Other indicators show sharp end-points.

substance	rough	first	second	third
at start	1.2	3.2	2.5	3.7
at end	28.2	29.6	29.0	30.1
titre	27.0			

Volume of acid reacting with 25.0 cm^3 of alkali

Indicator	Colour in alkali	Colour in acid
litmus	blue	red
phenolphthalein	pink	colourless
screened methyl orange	green	pink

D–C

- Indicators, such as phenolphthalein, screened methyl orange and litmus, which give a sudden colour change at the neutral point, make the end point in titrations very easy to spot.
- Mixed indicators, such as UI, are not used in titrations. UI gives a continuous colour change so it is much harder to see the end point.
- Titration is an accurate technique. If there are large differences in the readings, something is wrong. If the readings are close, then the technique is **reliable**.
- Small differences can be experimental error. Using the average reading allows for this.

Questions

Grades G-E

1 Which colour is Universal indicator in a solution of pH 14?

Grades D-C

2 Alkali is slowly added to acid. How does the pH change?

Grades G-E

3 Which two pieces of equipment used in a titration measure volumes accurately?

Grades D-C

4 Why are titrations carried out several times before a volume is decided?

Grades

Gas volumes

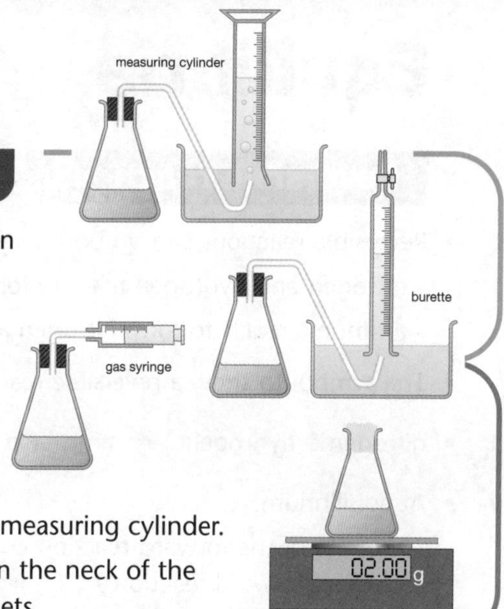

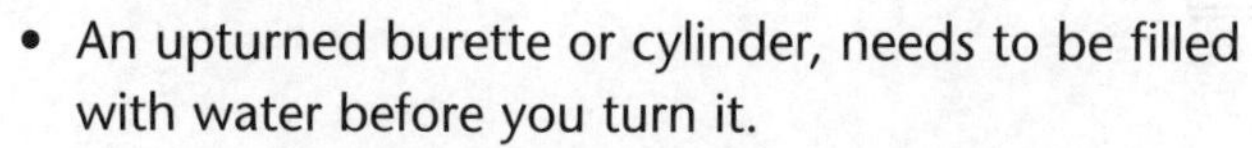

Measuring the gas made in a reaction

G–E

- The diagram shows three ways of collecting gas given off in a reaction. Reading off the scale finds the volume of gas.
- When using a balance, the mass drops as gas is given off.

D–C

- An upturned burette or cylinder, needs to be filled with water before you turn it.
- The volume is read off the scale on the side.
- The scale on a burette goes the opposite way to that on a measuring cylinder.
- When using a balance, a loose plug of cotton wool is put in the neck of the flask. This lets the gas out but not any spray of liquid droplets.

What can you tell from the results?

G–E

- Reactions start fast and then slow down.
- Reactions will only completely stop when one of the reactants is totally used up.
- If reactions that give off a gas have stopped – no more gas is given off.
- To increase the total amount of gas, just use more **reactant**.

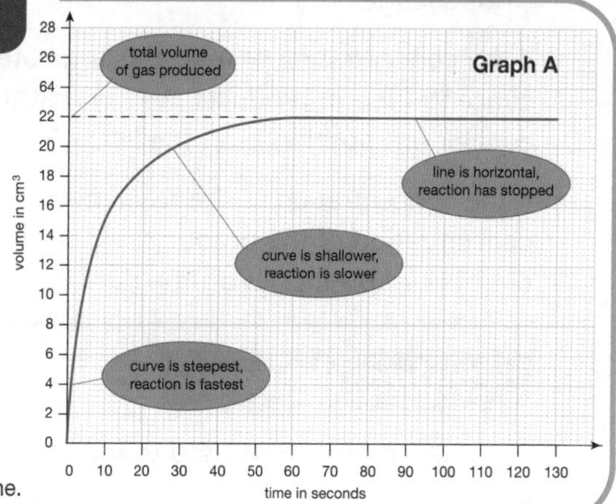

The volume of gas given off against time.

Changing the amounts of reactants

D–C

- When magnesium ribbon reacts with acid, hydrogen gas is given off. If you use exactly the right amounts, there is no magnesium ribbon left at the end, and all the acid is neutralised.
- If you use the same amount of acid but only half the amount of magnesium, you will only get half the gas. In this case we say the magnesium is the **limiting reactant**.
- The total amount of gas produced is directly proportional to the amount of the limiting reactant.

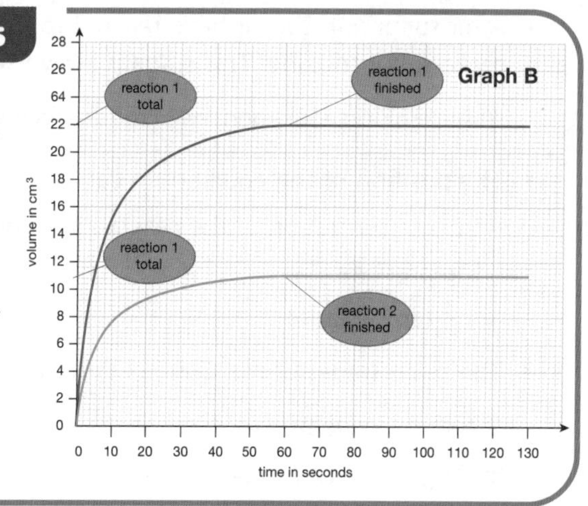

Questions

Grades G-E

1 Write down two ways of collecting a volume of 10 cm^3 of gas.

Grades D-C

2 What is the volume of gas collected in this gas syringe?

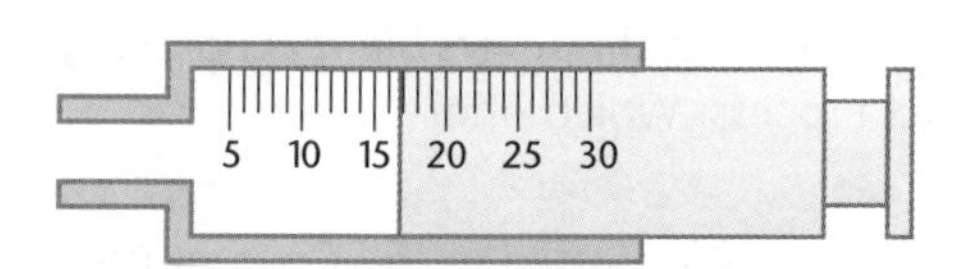

Grades G-E

3 Look at Graph A. How much gas was made by the end of the reaction?

Grades D-C

4 Explain why the two curves in Graph B are different.

Equilibria

Grades

Reversible reactions

G–E

- Reversible reactions can go both ways at the same time:
  - nitrogen and hydrogen react to form ammonia (forward reaction)
  - ammonia reacts to form nitrogen and hydrogen (backward reaction).
- The symbol to show a reversible reaction is ⇌ .
- nitrogen + hydrogen ⇌ ammonia

D–C

- At equilibrium:
  - the rate of the forward reaction equals the rate of the backward reaction
  - concentrations of reactants and of products do not change.
- If the concentration of reactants is greater than the concentration of products, we say that the equilibrium position is on the left.
- If the concentration of the reactants is less than the concentration of the products, we say that the equilibrium position is on the right.

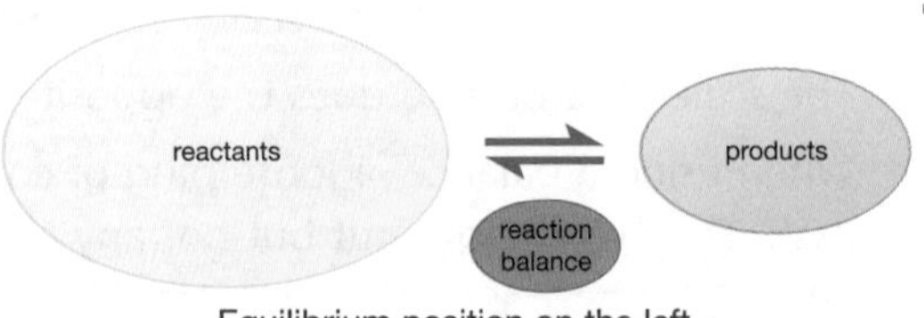

Equilibrium position on the left.

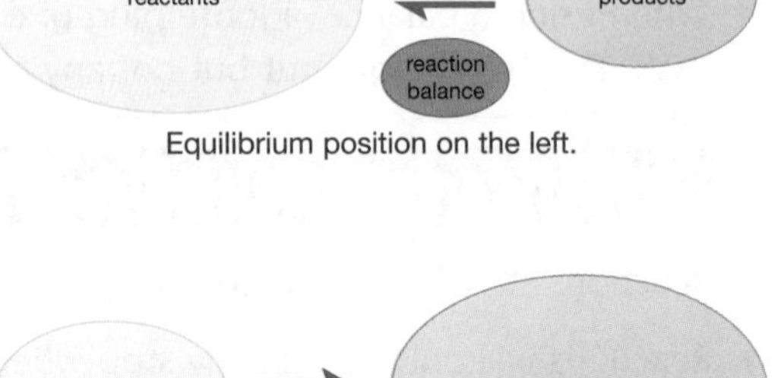

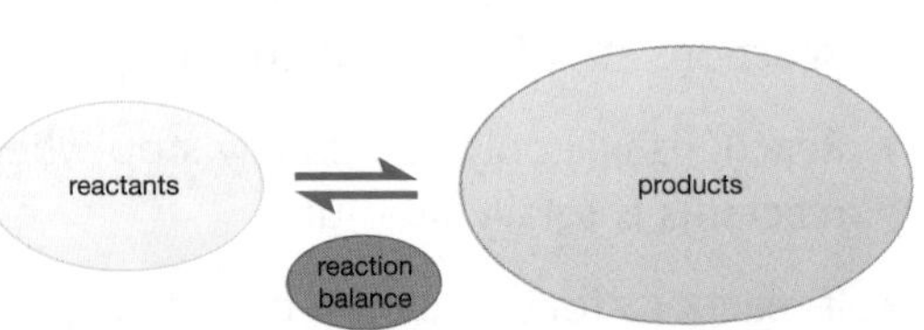

Equilibrium position on the right.

Contact Process

G–E

- A reversible reaction is used to make sulfuric acid – the Contact Process.
- Three raw materials are used: sulfur, air and water.
- After sulfur and the air have reacted to make sulfur dioxide, this then has to react with more air to make sulfur trioxide. This stage is a reversible reaction.

  sulfur dioxide + oxygen ⇌ sulfur trioxide

D–C

- The position of the equilibrium can be changed if you change:
  - the concentration of the reactants or the products
  - the pressure
  - the temperature.
- The main stages of the Contact Process are:

  1 sulfur + oxygen ⟶ sulfur dioxide

  2 sulfur dioxide + oxygen ⇌ sulfur trioxide

  3 sulfur trioxide + water ⟶ sulfuric acid
- Reaction 2 is the reversible reaction.
- For the most economic yield, the reaction is carried out at around 450 °C, at atmospheric pressure, using a catalyst of vanadium pentoxide, V_2O_5.

Questions

Grades G-E

1 Write down the symbol used for a reversible reaction.

Grades D-C

2 At equilibrium, the reaction A + B ⇌ 3C + 3D has 1 mole of A, 1 mole of B, 3 moles of C, 3 moles of D. Where is the position of equilibrium?

Grades G-E

3 A chemical is made in the reversible reaction stage of the Contact Process. Which one?

Grades D-C

4 What are the conditions used in the Contact Process?

Strong and weak acids

Strong and weak acids

G–E

- Not all acids are the same.
- Many acids in the lab are **strong acids**, e.g. hydrochloric acid, sulfuric acid and nitric acid.
- Acids you use in the home, such as ethanoic acid in vinegar, are **weak acids**.
- Strong acids can be concentrated or dilute.
- Weak acids can be concentrated or dilute.
- At the same concentrations, strong acids react faster than weak acids.
- Strong acids have a lower **pH**.

D–C

- Acids have hydrogen atoms in their formula, e.g. hydrochloric acid is HCl.
- In water the acid molecule ionises – it turns into ions.
  acid molecule ⟶ hydrogen ions + other ions
- The reactions of acids are caused by the hydrogen ions.
- Strong acids change completely into their ions when they are put into water.
  strong acid ⟶ hydrogen ions + other ions
  There are lots of hydrogen ions, so the acid seems **very acidic**.
- In weak acid only a few of the molecules change into ions when they are put into water.
  A reversible reaction is set up.
  weak acid ⇌ hydrogen ions + other ions
  The solution contains lots of acid molecules, but not many H^+ ions – so it does not seem to be so acidic.

Reactions with acids

G–E

- Both strong and weak acids react with magnesium to make hydrogen gas.
- Both react with calcium carbonate to make carbon dioxide gas.
- Ethanoic acid reacts more slowly than hydrochloric acid of the same concentration, though it produces just as much gas in the end.

D–C

- Strong and weak acids have the same reactions.
- The reactions of acids are due to the hydrogen ions.
- Some weak acids have so few hydrogen ions that they will only react with very reactive substances such as magnesium.
- Weak acids react more slowly than strong acids.
- Strong acids produce lots of H^+ ions; there are lots collisions between H^+ and the magnesium. Reactions are fast.
- Weak acids have fewer H^+, so fewer collisions. Reactions are slow.

Questions

Grades G-E

1 What is the difference between a strong acid and a weak acid?

Grades D-C

2 Strong acids break into their ions completely if put into water. What happens to weak acids when they are put into water?

Grades G-E

3 Magnesium reacts with hydrochloric acid. It makes 60 cm^3 of gas. How much gas would be made if the same amount of magnesium reacted with the same volume of ethanoic acid of the same concentration?

Grades D-C

4 One ion makes a solution into an acid. Which one?

Ionic equations

Grades

Precipitation reactions

G–E

- Two solutions react to make an insoluble solid. This solid is a **precipitate**.
- Ions from one compound swap with ions from another to make new substances.

lead nitrate solution + sodium iodide solution ⟶ lead iodide precipitate + sodium nitrate solution

- State symbols in an equation show which substance is a solid and which is a solution: (s) solid, (l) liquid, (aq) aqueous – dissolved in water, (g) gas.

lead nitrate$_{(aq)}$ + sodium iodide$_{(aq)}$ ⟶ lead iodide$_{(s)}$ + sodium nitrate$_{(aq)}$

- Precipitation reactions are used to see if particular ions are in a solution.
- Silver nitrate gives coloured precipitates with **halide** ions.
- Barium nitrate gives a white precipitate with **sulfate** ions.

ion	precipitate with silver nitrate
chloride	white
bromide	cream
iodide	yellow

D–C

- In solid ionic compounds, such as sodium chloride, the sodium ions and the chloride ions are held together in fixed positions; they cannot move about.
- When the ionic compound is melted or dissolved, the ions can move about.
- In the reaction of lead nitrate with sodium iodide there is only a reaction between lead ions and iodide ions. The sodium nitrate is the left over solution of ions at the end.

lead nitrate$_{(aq)}$ + sodium iodide$_{(aq)}$ ⟶ lead iodide$_{(s)}$ + sodium nitrate$_{(aq)}$

- To write equations for precipitation you have to know which compounds are insoluble.
- Insoluble compounds are: silver chloride, silver bromide, silver iodide, barium sulfate.

Preparing a clean dry sample of an insoluble salt by precipitation

G–E

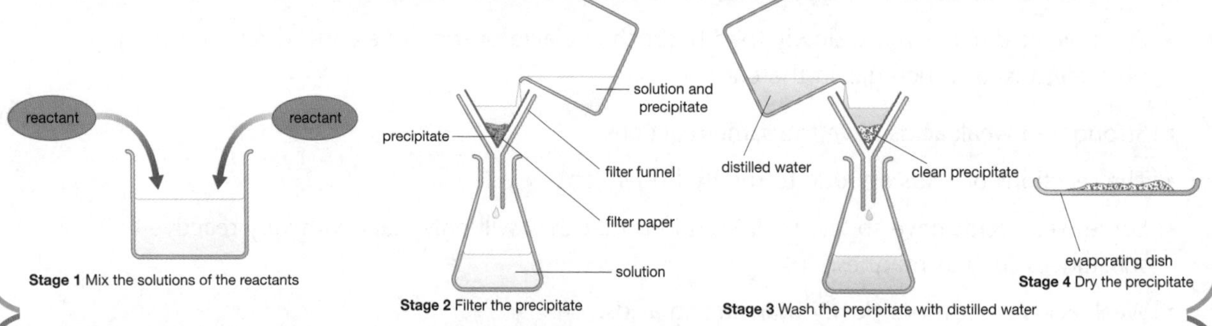

Stage 1 Mix the solutions of the reactants

Stage 2 Filter the precipitate

Stage 3 Wash the precipitate with distilled water

Stage 4 Dry the precipitate

D–C

- **Stage 1** Mix. The precipitate of lead chloride and a solution of sodium nitrate is made.
- **Stage 2** Filter. The precipitate is left with traces of the sodium nitrate solution.
- **Stage 3** Wash. Distilled water removes the traces of sodium nitrate solution.
- **Stage 4** Dry. The precipitate lead chloride is left in a warm place for the water to evaporate.

Questions

Grades G-E

1 What colour is the precipitate of silver iodide?

Grades D-C

2 Write a word equation for the reaction of silver nitrate and sodium iodide.

Grades G-E

3 How would you make a clean, dry sample of silver chloride?

Grades D-C

4 Why do you wash a precipitate in distilled water when making a dry sample?

C5 Summary

Moles and formulae

The mole is a unit for a standard amount of substance.

The mass of one mole of a substance is called its **molar mass**.
The molar mass of a substance is the relative formula mass in grams.

The **empirical formula** is the ratio of each type of atom present in the compound. An empirical formula must be a whole number ratio.

The **relative formula mass** of carbon monoxide, CO, is the sum of its atomic masses [C = 12, O = 16].

12 + 16 = 28

The empirical formula of $C_5H_{11}COOH$ is C_3H_6O.

Electrolysis

Positive ions discharge at the **cathode** (negative electrode). Negative ions discharge at the **anode** (positive electrode).

Molten lead bromide **decomposes** in electrolysis to make lead metal and bromine gas.

The amount of substance produced at each electrode increases as current increases and as time increases.

Electric current is a flow of charge.
Electrolytes are ionic

The charge moves through an electrolyte as the **ions** can move.
If the electrolyte is solid then the ions cannot move and the **current** cannot flow.

Titrations

Acids have **low** pH.
Alkalis have **high** pH.
Adding acid **lowers** the pH.
Adding alkali **increases** the pH.

When acid is added to alkali a salt is made.

acid + alkali ⟶ salt + water

When an acid reacts with an alkali, the pH of the solution changes.

When there is just alkali at the start, the **pH** number is high. As acid is added, it starts to neutralise the alkali and the pH falls.

Equilibria

Reversible reactions can go both ways at the same time. The symbol to show a reversible reaction is $\rightleftharpoons$.

Nitrogen and hydrogen react to form ammonia (**forward reaction**) and ammonia reacts to form nitrogen and hydrogen (**backward reaction**).

nitrogen + hydrogen $\rightleftharpoons$ ammonia

If the **concentration** of reactants is greater than the concentration of products, we say that the **equilibrium position** is on the left.

The position of the equilibrium can be changed if you change the concentration of the reactants or the products, the pressure or the temperature.

Energy transfers – fuel cells

Grades

Electric current from fuel cells

G–E

- Hydrogen and oxygen can be used in a **fuel cell** to produce an electric current.
- They do not need replacing or recharging but they have a fuel tank that needs refilling.
- Fuel cells are very efficient at producing electric current as they have no moving parts.
- The fuel in the fuel cell reacts with oxygen from the air.
- Hydrogen makes water when it reacts with oxygen, so is a pollution-free fuel.
- Fuel cells can be used to provide electrical power in spacecraft.

D–C

- Fuel cells are used in spacecraft because they:
  - are efficient as they waste very little energy
  - are lighter than normal batteries, so the spacecraft can carry a bigger payload
  - can be used continuously as they don't need time out to be recharged
  - don't need a special fuel with its own separate storage system; the spacecraft has to carry hydrogen and oxygen anyway for the rocket engines
  - produce water that is used by the astronauts for drinking.
- Car makers are very interested in fuel cells as more laws are being passed to reduce the pollution from vehicle exhausts and petrol reserves will eventually run out.
- A normal car engine converts chemical energy into heat, and the heat is then converted to movement energy. This stage is inefficient, and when fuels burn the temperature gets hot enough to react the nitrogen and oxygen in the air to make nitrogen oxides. Nitrogen oxides in the air cause photochemical smog.
- Cars powered by fuel cells are more efficient than normal engines so they use less fuel. The fuel does not burn, so no high temperatures are involved and no oxides of nitrogen are produced. The main product of the hydrogen-powered fuel cell is water, which is not a pollutant at all.
- A problem with cars powered by fuel cells is that hydrogen is a gas. This is more difficult to store inside the car, and filling stations will need a totally different type of fuel pump.

Reactions of hydrogen and oxygen

G–E

- Oxygen and hydrogen are both invisible gases.
- If a glowing splint is put into a test tube of oxygen, the glowing splint will relight.
- If a lighted splint is put into a test tube of hydrogen, there will be a squeaky 'pop'.

D–C

- Energy is only released when fuel reacts with oxygen from the air.
- A reaction which gives out energy is exothermic.
- The reaction between hydrogen and oxygen is **exothermic**.
- In a fuel cell that uses hydrogen, the reaction is:
  hydrogen + oxygen ⟶ water
- If hydrogen reacts with oxygen by burning, the chemical energy is given out as heat.
- A fuel cell converts chemical energy directly into electrical energy – there is no heat loss.

Questions

Grades G-E

1 Why is hydrogen a pollution-free fuel?

Grades D-C

2 Give two reasons why the car industry wants to develop fuel cells.

Grades G-E

3 How would you test a tube of gas to see if it is oxygen?

Grades D-C

4 Why is the reaction between hydrogen and oxygen described as 'exothermic'?

Redox reactions

Grades

Rusting iron

G–E

- Iron rusts when oxygen (or air) and water are touching the surface of the iron.
- Rust is hydrated iron(III) oxide.
- Six ways of preventing rust are: covering the iron with oil or grease; covering the iron with paint; covering the iron with **tin plate**; **galvanising** the iron by covering with a layer of zinc; **sacrificial protection** – connect the iron to a reactive metal which will corrode instead of the iron; mixing other elements in with the iron to make an **alloy**.

Rusting and redox

D–C

- Rusting is a redox reaction.
  iron + oxygen + water ⟶ hydrated iron(III) oxide
- In redox reactions something is oxidised and something else is reduced.
- To stop iron rusting, one of the reactants must be taken out of the equation: water must not touch the iron; iron will not rust in air if the air is very dry; oxygen must not touch the iron.
- Covering the iron with a layer of oil, grease or paint stops the iron rusting because they stop oxygen or water from reaching the surface of the iron.

Displacement reactions

G–E

- If we put magnesium into iron sulfate solution, the magnesium will push the iron out of the iron sulfate.
- We will have solid iron and a solution of magnesium sulfate. The solution will get hot.
- This is called a **displacement reaction**. The iron that has been pushed out has been displaced.
- It happens because magnesium is more reactive than iron.
- When four different metals are put in different solutions this happens:

	metal being added			
solution used	**magnesium**	**zinc**	**iron**	**tin**
magnesium sulfate	✗	✗	✗	✗
zinc sulfate	✓	✗	✗	✗
iron sulfate	✓	✓	✗	✗
tin sulfate	✓	✓	✓	✗

key:
✗ means that nothing happens
✓ means that the metal gets coated

- The table shows us that the order of reactivity is:

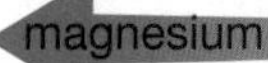

D–C

- Word equations for displacement reactions show that the more reactive metal 'swaps places' with the less reactive metal. Magnesium is more reactive than zinc.

  magnesium + zinc sulfate ⟶ magnesium sulfate + zinc
  (magnesium ↓ more reactive metal; zinc ↓ less reactive metal)

- As the order of reactivity is magnesium, zinc, iron, tin:
  – magnesium metal will displace zinc, iron and tin
  – zinc will displace iron and tin
  – iron will displace tin.

Questions

Grades G-E

1 Write down three ways to prevent rust.

Grades D-C

2 Why does painting prevent rust?

Grades G-E

3 If zinc is put into a solution of tin sulfate, why will the solution get hot?

Grades D-C

4 Write a word equation for the reaction between zinc and iron nitrate.

Alcohols

Fermentation

G–E

- The alcohols are a group of compounds. The most common alcohol is ethanol.
- Ethanol is used as a solvent, as a fuel for cars and as a beverage.
- Most ethanol is made from plants by **fermentation**. Plants are renewable, so ethanol made this way is a **renewable** fuel.
- During fermentation, yeast breaks down sugars in the plants to produce the ethanol. Yeast only does this if there is no air present.
- Fermentation needs:
  - sugars from plants
  - water
  - enzymes from yeast
  - a temperature between 25 and 50 °C
  - the absence of oxygen.

Ethanol is in alcoholic drinks

D–C

- The word equation for fermentation is:

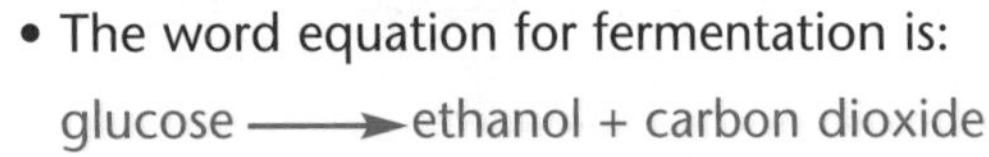
glucose ⟶ ethanol + carbon dioxide

- An optimum temperature between 25 and 50 °C is needed for fermentation.
- The ethanol produced is dilute. The solution is distilled get more ethanol.
- The **molecular formula** for ethanol is C_2H_6O (often written as C_2H_5OH).
- The **displayed formula** for ethanol is:

```
    H   H
    |   |
H — C — C — O — H
    |   |
    H   H
```

Making ethanol from ethene

G–E

- Most of the world's ethanol is made from biomass.
- Ethanol can also be made from **ethene**.
- Ethene is made from crude oil or from natural gas.
- Ethanol is made by reacting ethene with water. This is a **hydration reaction**.
- Ethanol can also be made back into ethene. This reaction 'loses' water. This is a **dehydration** reaction.

D–C

- Ethanol which is used industrially can be made from ethene by a hydration reaction.

  ethene + water ⟶ ethanol
- Ethene and steam are passed over a hot phosphoric acid catalyst.
- To dehydrate the ethanol, the vapour is passed over a hot aluminium oxide catalyst.

  ethanol ⟶ ethene + water

Questions

Grades G-E

1 Write down three things needed for fermentation.

Grades D-C

2 What is the word equation for the production of ethanol from sugars?

Grades G-E

3 In which way, other than fermentation, can ethanol be made?

Grades D-C

4 What is the catalyst needed for the dehydration of ethanol?

Chemistry of sodium chloride (NaCl)

Salt

- Salt (sodium chloride) is a raw material.
- Large amounts of **rock salt** are scattered on roads every winter.
- When molten sodium chloride is electrolysed, it splits into sodium and chlorine.

D–C

- Rock formations with salt deposits exist in the UK. Cheshire has the main salt mines.
- The salt may be extracted from the rock by using underground cutting machines. This impure salt is called rock salt and is used for gritting roads.
- Salt is also extracted by drilling a borehole down into the salt layer and pumping water down. The salt dissolves and is pumped up. The water is evaporated leaving table salt.
- Once the salt is removed from a mine, the ground may subside, which used to be a major problem. Some houses in these areas had steel frames to protect them if the ground did start to move. Nowadays mining is much more carefully controlled.

Electrolysis of sodium chloride solution

- Electrolysing a solution of salt is not the same as electrolysing the molten salt: electrolysis of molten sodium chloride gives chlorine and sodium; electrolysis of a concentrated solution of sodium chloride gives chlorine and hydrogen.
- Hydrogen is used to make margarine.
- Chlorine is used to sterilise drinking water supplies, and to make bleach, solvents, and plastics such as pvc.
- A test for chlorine is that litmus paper will be bleached.

D–C

- Sodium chloride solution is also known as **brine**.
- When brine is electrolysed, hydrogen is discharged from the water and chlorine from the sodium chloride, leaving sodium hydroxide in solution:
  water + sodium chloride ⟶ hydrogen + chlorine + sodium hydroxide
  – the sodium chloride must be a concentrated solution in water
  – the electrodes must be inert
  – hydrogen is produced at the cathode
  – chlorine is produced at the anode
  – sodium hydroxide solution is formed in the cell.
- Hydrogen and chlorine react explosively, so the electrolysis cell keeps the two chemicals apart.
- A porous barrier in the middle of the cell allows the ions to move but separates the gases.
- Chlorine is a powerful bleach. It is also a highly poisonous gas.
- Chlorine can be reacted with sodium hydroxide to make a much safer substance which releases chlorine easily when it is needed. Household bleaches are made in this way.

Electrolysis of a brine cell.

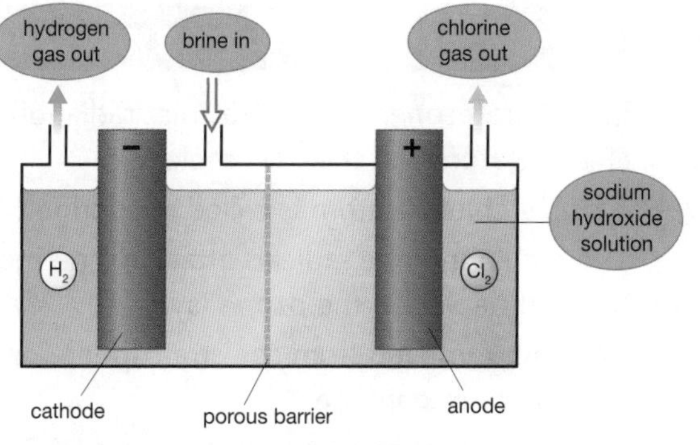

Questions

Grades G-E

1 What are the products of electrolysis of molten sodium chloride?

Grades D-C

2 What are the different ways that table salt and gritting salt are made?

Grades G-E

3 Write down three uses of chlorine.

Grades D-C

4 Why is a barrier used in the cell for the electrolysis of brine?

Depletion of the ozone layer

Grades

The ozone layer

G–E

- About 16 miles up in the atmosphere there is a very thin layer of **ozone**.
- This ozone stops some of the **ultraviolet** light from the Sun reaching us.
- Ultraviolet light is the part of sunlight that gives us a tan and an increased risk of getting sunburnt or 'ageing' skin.
- It can also increase the risk of getting skin cancer and cataracts of the eyes.
- Molecules with two oxygen atoms make oxygen gas.
- Molecules with three oxygen atoms make a different gas – ozone.
- CFCs have been destroying the ozone layer.
- More ultraviolet rays are getting through. CFCs are now banned in the UK.
- **Hydrocarbons** are a safer alternative, but they are not quite as good.

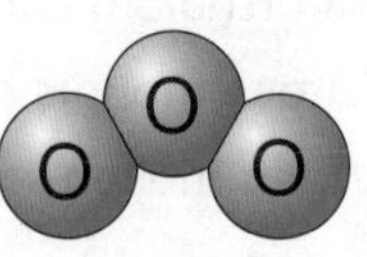

ozone molecule

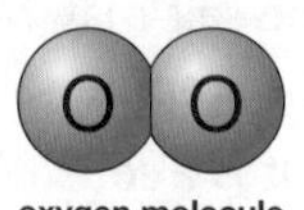

oxygen molecule

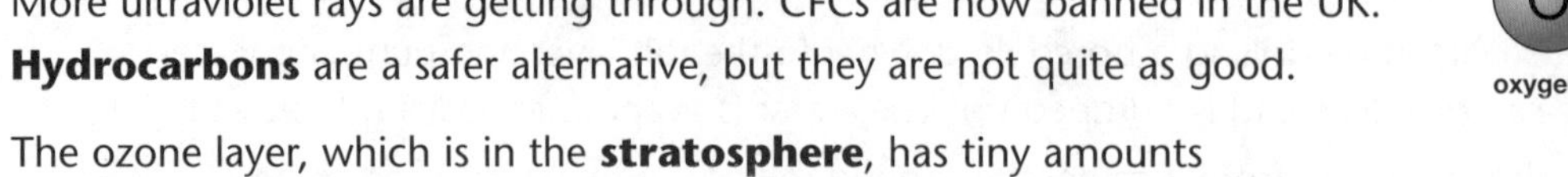

D–C

- The ozone layer, which is in the **stratosphere**, has tiny amounts of ozone.
- In 1985, scientists discovered that the amount of ozone high over the South Pole was much less than it should be, and they called this the 'hole' in the ozone layer.
- The more depleted the ozone layer gets, the more ultraviolet rays reach the Earth.
- When CFCs were first discovered, they were thought to be totally safe. We now know that these molecules slowly move up into the stratosphere where they 'attack' the ozone layer.
- CFCs are now banned.

What are CFCs?

G–E

- CFC stands for chlorofluorocarbon. They are organic molecules made from carbon, chlorine and fluorine atoms and nothing else.
- CFCs were used:
  - as refrigerants, a liquid which is pumped through pipes in the back of the fridge
  - as aerosol propellants, to push liquid out of aerosol cans
  - to make the tiny bubbles in foam plastic – blowing agents.
- All CFCs have low boiling points, are chemically inert and are insoluble in water.

CFCs, ozone and free radicals

D–C

- In the stratosphere, the ultraviolet radiation from the Sun is strong enough to break single chlorine atoms off the CFC molecule.
- A single chlorine atom is called a chlorine **free radical**.
- These chlorine free radicals attack ozone molecules, turning the ozone back into oxygen gas and depleting the ozone layer.
- CFCs are removed from the stratosphere only very slowly, so each CFC molecule has time to do a lot of damage.
- The main alternatives are alkanes and HFCs, hydrofluorocarbons.
- HFCs cannot make chlorine free radicals, so they are safer.

Questions

Grades G-E

1 What problems can be caused by increased levels of UV light?

Grades D-C

2 How do the levels of UV light change when there is a depletion of ozone?

Grades G-E

3 What two things were CFCs mainly used for?

Grades D-C

4 How does a single chlorine atom cause the ozone to be destroyed?

Hardness of water

Grades

Hard water

G–E

- It is very difficult for soap to make bubbles (to lather) in hard water.
- Hardness is caused by calcium or magnesium ions dissolved in the water.
- The soap reacts with the ions to make a solid scum. Once the soap has reacted with all the ions, the rest of the soap will work to make a lather for washing.
- Soapless detergents do the same job as soap, but they aren't affected by hard water.
- There are two types of hard water:
  – temporary, the hardness can be removed by boiling the water
  – permanent, boiling the water has no effect on the hardness.

D–C

- Permanent hardness is produced when calcium sulfate dissolves in water.
- Temporary hardness is produced when water with dissolved carbon dioxide from the air reacts with calcium carbonate. Together they form calcium hydrogencarbonate.
  calcium carbonate + carbon dioxide + water ⟶ calcium hydrogencarbonate
- The hardness in samples of water can be compared by measuring how much soap reacts.
- When you shake a soap flake with a water sample, the calcium ions in the water will react with the soap and turn it into scum.
- As you shake in more flakes, eventually all of the calcium ions will have reacted with the soap.
- After that, any more soap will produce a stable lather for the first time.
- The number of soap flakes used tells you how hard the water is.

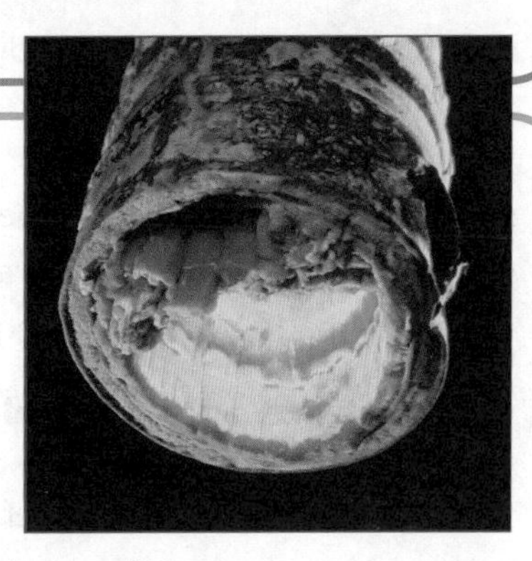

Removing hardness

G–E

- Hardness in water can be removed by using washing soda or ion exchange columns.
- Machine water softeners have ion exchange columns inside them to remove hardness.
- If you don't soften water before you heat it, kettles and hot-water pipes will clog up with solid white limescale.
- Descalers get the limescale out of kettles. Limescale is made of calcium carbonate.
- Descalers contain acids which will react with the calcium carbonate.

D–C

- Calcium hydrogencarbonate decomposes on heating to insoluble calcium carbonate, water and carbon dioxide. This makes a solid deposit of limescale inside hot water pipes.
- Permanent hardness is not affected by heating. The calcium sulfate is too stable.
- Ion exchange resins are used to remove hardness. The water flows over solid resin. The resin traps calcium and magnesium ions on to it, taking these ions out of the water.
- Ion exchange resins remove both temporary and permanent hardness.
- Strong acids such as hydrochloric acid remove the limescale, but might react with tap metal.
- Descalers contain weak acids which are less likely to damage anything else.
  acid + carbonate ⟶ salt + carbon dioxide + water

Questions

Grades G-E

1 Which type of hardness of water is not affected by boiling?

Grades D-C

2 Why does calcium carbonate dissolve in rain water but not in pure water?

Grades G-E

3 From which kind of chemical are descalers made?

Grades D-C

4 Which kind of hardness of water do ion exchange resins remove?

Natural fats and oils

Grades

Fats and oils

G–E

- Natural **fats** and **oils** are important **raw materials** in the chemical industry. They are used to make margarine and soap.
- Vegetable oils can be made into **biodiesel** as an alternative to diesel from crude oil.
- Fats and oils come from animals and plants. They are the same type of chemical.
- Oils are liquid at room temperature and come from plants, e.g. olives and sunflowers.
- Fats are solid. Butter comes from cows' milk. Bacon fat gives us lard.

D–C

- Fats and oils are compounds called **esters**. They are made of chains of carbon atoms.
- Bromine water is orange. If it is shaken with an unsaturated compound it loses its colour. It is decolourised. This is a test for unsaturation.
- One use of vegetable oils is to make margarine. Vegetable oils are unsaturated.

if all the carbon atoms in a chain are linked by single bonds the compound is **saturated**

```
  H  H  H  H  H  H  H
  |  |  |  |  |  |  |
 -C--C--C--C--C--C--C-
  |  |  |  |  |  |  |
  H  H  H  H  H  H  H
```

some fats and oils have carbon that contain one or more **double bonds**, the compounds are **unsaturated**

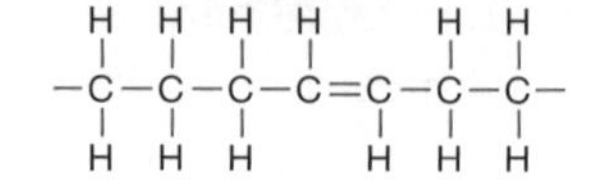

- The first stage is to 'harden' them and turn them into saturated compounds.
- Hydrogen is bubbled through the oil at about 200 °C using a nickel catalyst.
- The hydrogen reacts with the double bonds and turns them into single bonds.

Mixing oil and water

G–E

- Fats and oils will not normally mix with water. If you shake oil and water together tiny droplets of oil will spread through the water. The oil drops are dispersed through the water.
- These are called **emulsions**. Milk is an oil-in-water emulsion.
- Butter is made of water dispersed through oil or fat. It is a water-in-oil emulsion.
- Fats and oils will mix with water much more easily if we use soap.
- Soap is made by reacting vegetable oils with sodium hydroxide.

D–C

- Oil and water are **immiscible** liquids. They do not mix. They do not dissolve in each other, but it is possible to disperse tiny droplets of one liquid inside the other.
- Water and oil can make two types of emulsion as shown in the diagram.
- Oil and water can be made to mix as an emulsion by using an **emulsifier**.

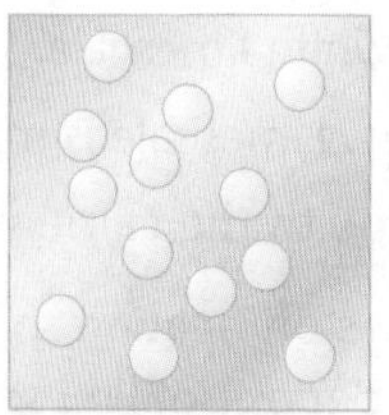

water–in–oil emulsion contains droplets of water spread through oil

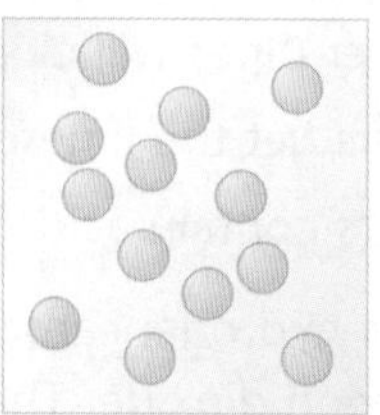

oil–on–water emulsion contains droplets of oil spread through water

- Fats and oils are difficult to wash from clothes because they do not dissolve in water.
- Fats and oils are used to make soap when they are split up by hot sodium hydroxide.
  fat + sodium hydroxide ⟶ soap + glycerol
- In soap manufacture, vegetable oils are heated in large vats with sodium hydroxide solution – saponification.
- Salt is added at the end of the reaction to make the soap precipitate out.
- The solid soap can be removed and then colouring and perfume may be added.

Questions

Grades G-E

1 From which other substance can diesel be made apart from crude oil?

Grades D-C

2 How is bromine used to test for unsaturation?

Grades G-E

3 What kind of emulsion is butter?

Grades D-C

4 What happens during saponification?

Analgesics

Grades

Medicines

G–E

- Medicines are chemicals, the most common are **analgesics**. They reduce pain.
- Most medicines are bought from a chemist called a **pharmacist**, who is trained to give advice on a wide range of simple problems.
- Almost all painkillers that you can buy in pharmacies are based on three analgesic drugs: aspirin, paracetamol or ibuprofen. The most common of these is aspirin.

D–C

- The active ingredients of medicines are **drugs**. A drug is any externally administered chemical which affects the body's chemical reactions. We say 'externally administered' because the body also produces chemicals of its own which affect its reactions.
- The chemicals used to make the analgesics are very pure.
- An overdose of aspirin causes severe bleeding in the stomach.
- An overdose of paracetamol causes liver damage.
- If several drugs are being taken, the drugs may interfere with each other. It is always important to warn your doctor if you are already taking any other medicine.

The beneficial effects of aspirin

G–E

- Aspirin relieves pain and also lowers the body temperature, so reducing fever.
- Aspirin, in small doses, reduces the risk of heart attack.
- It thins the blood, which helps prevent blood clots forming. Low-dose aspirin is available.
- For thousands of years people have known that a herbal tea made from willow bark relieves fever and reduces pain.
- The active ingredient is **salicylic acid**, which causes severe irritation to the lining of people's stomach. In 1895, Felix Hofmann altered the salicylic acid to make aspirin.
- Nowadays, rather than taking the bark from trees, we manufacture aspirin synthetically.

Formulae

D–C

- The molecular formula of paracetamol is $C_8H_9NO_2$.
- Aspirin is now sold in the form of soluble aspirin.
- Soluble aspirin dissolves in a glass of water, which makes it easier to swallow and faster to act. It also has fewer side effects than aspirin itself.

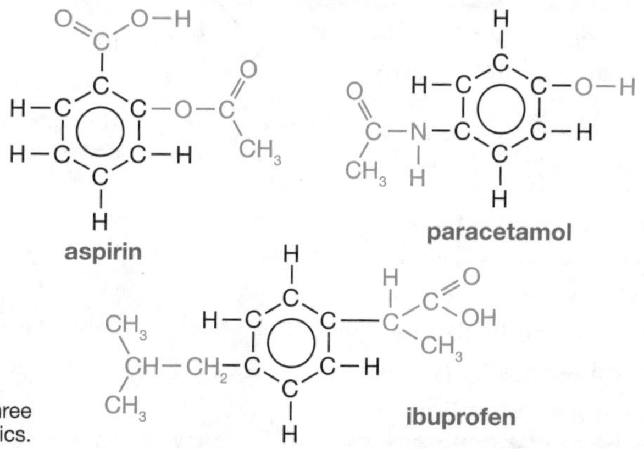

aspirin

paracetamol

ibuprofen

The formulae of three common analgesics.

Questions

Grades G-E

1 What are the three most common analgesics?

Grades D-C

2 What is the danger of an overdose of paracetamol?

Grades G-E

3 Write about three ways that aspirin can help relieve illness.

Grades D-C

4 What is the molecular formula of ibruprofen?

C6 Summary

Fuel cells

Hydrogen burns with a squeaky pop when a lighted splint is put into a test tube of the gas.

Oxygen relights a glowing splint when it is put into a test tube of the gas.

A fuel cell is supplied with hydrogen and oxygen and uses the energy from the reaction between them to create **electrical energy**.

The reaction between hydrogen and oxygen gives out energy to the surroundings. It is an **exothermic reaction**.

Fuel cells are used to give electrical power in spacecraft.

Alcohols

This is the equation for **fermentation**:
glucose ⟶ carbon dioxide + ethanol

The conditions needed for **fermentation** are:
- 25–50 °C
- presence of water
- enzymes found in yeast
- no oxygen.

Alcohol can also be made from ethene.
ethene + water ⟶ ethanol

The **molecular formula** of ethanol is C_2H_6O.
The **displayed formula** of ethanol is:

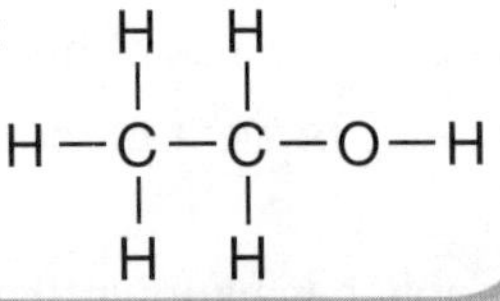

```
    H   H
    |   |
H — C — C — O — H
    |   |
    H   H
```

Dehydration of ethanol makes ethene.

Ethanol can be dehydrated to make ethene by passing ethanol vapour over a heated catalyst. The catalyst is aluminium oxide.
ethanol ⟶ ethene + water

The ozone layer

CFCs have been banned in the UK as they lead to the depletion of the **ozone** layer.

CFCs are used as refrigerants and aerosol propellants.

Ultraviolet light on CFCs makes **chlorine** atoms. In the **stratosphere** this leads to the depletion of the ozone layer.

More **ultraviolet** light can reach the surface of the Earth if the ozone layer is depleted.

Increased levels of UV can lead to an increased risk of sunburn and skin cancer.

Analgesics

A **drug** is an externally administered substance which modifies or affects chemical reactions in the body.

Analgesics, such as aspirin are painkillers and reduce pain.
Aspirin lowers the body temperature quickly.
Aspirin also thins the blood to reduce risks of blood clots.

Aspirin was first discovered in willow bark.
Aspirin is now manufactured synthetically.

This is the displayed formula of aspirin

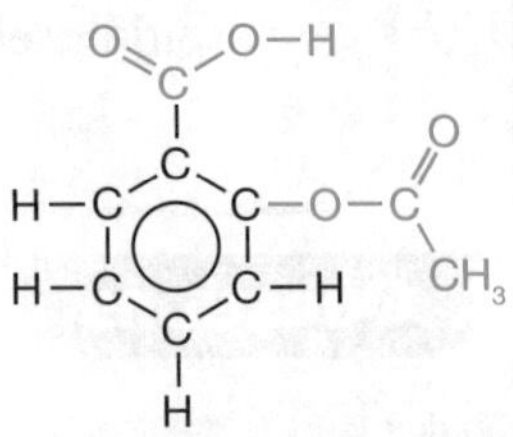

How science works

Understanding the scientific process

As part of your Chemistry assessment, you will need to show that you have an understanding of the scientific process – How Science Works.

This involves examining how scientific data is collected and analysed. You will need to evaluate the data by providing evidence to test ideas and develop theories. Some explanations are developed using scientific theories, models and ideas. You should be aware that there are some questions science cannot answer.

Collecting and evaluating data

You should be able to devise a plan that will answer a scientific question or solve a scientific problem. In doing so, you will need to collect data from both primary and secondary sources. Primary data will come from your own findings – often from an experimental investigation. Whilst working with primary data, you will need to show that you can work safely and accurately, not only on your own but also with others.

Secondary data is found by research – often using ICT but do not forget books, journals, magazines and newspapers are also sources of secondary data. The data you collect will need to be evaluated for its validity and reliability.

Presenting information

You should be able to present your information in an appropriate, scientific manner. This means being able to develop an argument and come to a conclusion based on recall and analysis of scientific information. It is important to use both quantitative and qualitative arguments.

Changing ideas and explanations

Many of today's scientific and technological developments have both benefits and risks. The decisions that scientists make will almost certainly raise ethical, environmental, social or economic questions. Scientific ideas and explanations change as time passes and it is the job of scientists to validate these changing ideas.

In 1692, the British astronomer Edmund Halley (after whom Halley's Comet was named) suggested that the Earth consisted of four concentric spheres. He was trying to explain the magnetic field that surrounds the Earth. There was, he said, a shell about 500 miles thick, two inner concentric shells and an inner core. The shells were separated by atmospheres and each shell had magnetic poles. The spheres rotated at different speeds. He believed this explained why unusual compass readings occurred. He also believed that each of these inner spheres supported life which was constantly lit by a luminous atmosphere.

This may sound quite an absurd idea today, but it is the work of scientists for the past 300 years that has developed different models that are constantly being refined.

How science works

Science in the News

Assessment

Science in the News is intended as the main way in which the OCR Chemistry course assesses your understanding of How Science Works.

Whilst some of you will continue to study science, many of you will have completed your science education by the time you have finished your GCSE course. It is important that you are able to meet any scientific challenge which arises in later life.

It is important that you realise when data or information is not presented in an accurate way. Think about what is wrong in this example based on a newspaper article.

Acid Alert Closes Motorway

by John Smith

The M6 motorway near Stafford was closed earlier today after a tanker carrying 20 tonnes of highly acidic sodium hydroxide solution started to leak some of the contents.

Awareness of current issues

You should also be aware of what aspects of science may be important for people living in the 21st Century.

One of the most controversial topics at this time is the most effective use of the dwindling supplies of crude oil.

Your Science in the News assessment will ask you to undertake some research on a scientific issue. The task set to you will be in the form of a question. You will then have to produce a short report which will clearly show that you have

- considered both sides of the argument
- decided on the suitability, accuracy and/or reliability of the evidence
- considered the impact on society and the environment
- justified your conclusion about the question asked.

The aim is to equip you with life-long skills that will allow you to take a full and active part in the scientific 21st Century.

Collins

Collins Revision

GCSE Foundation Chemistry

Exam Practice Workbook

FOR OCR GATEWAY B

Fundamental concepts

Grades

1 a In the chemical reaction **A + B → C + D**

i write down the reactants ______________________ [1 mark] G–E

ii write down the products ______________________ [1 mark]

b i Write down the **word** equation for the reaction between magnesium (Mg) and oxygen (O_2) to make magnesium oxide (MgO).

____

______________________ [2 marks]

ii Construct a **balanced symbol** equation for this reaction. D–C

____

______________________ [2 marks]

2 a Look at the formula for copper sulfate: **$CuSO_4$**.

i How many different elements are there in $CuSO_4$? ______________________ [1 mark] G–E

ii What is the **total** number of atoms in $CuSO_4$? ______________________ [1 mark]

iii What is the number of atoms of each different element?

______________________ [2 marks]

b Write down the total number of atoms in the formula of copper nitrate: **$Cu(NO_3)_2$**. D–C

______________________ [1 mark]

3 Look at the list: H_2 S O_2 H_2O Cu $CuSO_4$

a Write down the **elements** from the list.

______________________ [1 mark] G–E

b Write down the **compounds** from the list.

______________________ [1 mark]

c Write down which are **molecules** from the list.

______________________ [1 mark]

4 a Look at the displayed formula of ethanoic acid. G–E

$$H-\underset{\underset{H}{|}}{\overset{\overset{H}{|}}{C}}-C\begin{matrix}\nearrow O \\ \searrow O-H\end{matrix}$$

In the formula:

i How many **C** atoms are there? ______________________

ii How many **H** atoms are there? ______________________

iii How many **O** atoms are there? ______________________

iv How many different elements are in the formula? ______________________ [4 marks] D–C

b Write down the molecular formula of ethanoic acid. ______________________ [1 mark]

c Atoms in this acid are held together by covalent bonds. What is the other **type** of bond?

______________________ [1 mark]

Grades

Cooking

G–E

1 a There are many different ways to cook food. Write down **three** ways.

____

____

______________________________ [3 marks]

D–C

b Some foods need to be cooked. Explain why.

____

______________________________ [2 marks]

G–E

2 a Cooking food is an example of a chemical change. Finish the sentences to explain why. Choose the **best** words from this list.

energy **irreversible** **reactant** **reversible** **substance**

The change is ____________ . An____________ change takes place in the food. A new ____________ is made. [3 marks]

D–C

b What happens to protein molecules when they are cooked?

______________________________ [1 mark]

G–E

3 a This is a question about making cakes rise. Finish the sentences. Choose the **best** words from this list.

baking powder **carbon dioxide** **dissolved** **heated** **nitrogen**

____________ is added to make cakes rise. It gives off ____________ when it is ____________ . [3 marks]

D–C

b Baking powder is a chemical called **sodium hydrogencarbonate**. When it is heated it **decomposes** to give sodium carbonate, carbon dioxide and water.

i Write down the word equation for the reaction.

______________________________ [1 mark]

ii Write down the **reactant** of the reaction.

______________________________ [1 mark]

iii Write down a **product** of the reaction.

______________________________ [1 mark]

G–E

4 The chemical test for carbon dioxide is to pass it through limewater. It will turn the limewater from ____________ to ____________ .

carbon dioxide

delivery tube

limewater

[2 marks]

Food additives

Grades

1 a What is all food made from? Put a (ring) around the correct answer. G–E

additives **chemicals** **emulsifiers** **fibres** **proteins** [1 mark]

b What are the main types of food additives? Put a (ring) around the **four** correct answers.

antioxidants **carbohydrates** **emulsifiers** **fibres** **flavour enhancers**

food colours **proteins** **sugars** [4 marks]

c Why are antioxidants added to tinned fruit?

____ [1 mark]

d Why was the yellow food colour, tartrazine, taken out of most sweets for children?

____ [1 mark]

e Ascorbic acid (vitamin C) is used as an antioxidant in which foods? D–C

____

____ [2 marks]

f Write down **one** reason why additives are used.

____ [1 mark]

2 a Put these ingredients in order on the food label. G–E

Sugar 6.0 g
Salt 0.2 g
Wheat 14.0 g

ingredient	typical value per 100g

[2 marks]

b Why is food packaging used?

____ [1 mark]

c What is active packaging? D–C

____ [1 mark]

d What is intelligent packaging?

____ [1 mark]

3 a Oil and water do not mix. What needs to be added to clean oily plates? G–E

____ [1 mark]

b Look at the diagram. D–C
It is a detergent molecule made up of two parts, a head and a tail. Describe how the detergent works on removing grease in water. Use the word **emulsifier** in your answer. Use the diagram to help you.

____

____

____

______________________________________ [5 marks]

c Write down **one** example of an **emulsion**.

____ [1 mark]

Smells

G–E

1 a Write down **two** sources of natural perfume.

____

______________________________ [2 marks]

b How is the perfume extracted? Put a (ring) around the correct answer.

boiled **distilled** **filtered** **frozen** **stirred** [1 mark]

D–C

c i Some people object to cosmetics being tested on animals. Explain why.

______________________________ [1 mark]

ii Some people say cosmetics should be tested on animals. Explain why.

______________________________ [1 mark]

G–E

2 a A good perfume needs to have several properties. These are listed in the boxes. Draw a **straight** line to match the **best** reason to the property needed.

Property	Reason
evaporates easily	it can be put directly on the skin
non-toxic	its particles can reach the nose
insoluble in water	it does not poison people
does not irritate the skin	it cannot be washed off easily

[3 marks]

b What do perfumes stimulate to allow us to smell them?

______________________________ [1 mark]

D–C

3 a To make a perfume, alcohol is mixed with an acid to make an ester.

i Write down a word equation for this reaction.

______________________________ [2 marks]

ii Look at the diagram. Label the alcohol and acid. [1 mark]

iii Label the condenser. [1 mark]

iv What is happening at X?

____

______________________________ [1 mark]

X

v Why is the condenser used?

____

____

______________________________ [1 mark]

b Write down the name of the ester that is made from ethanoic acid and butanol.

______________________________ [1 mark]

G–E

4 a Finish these sentences by choosing the **best** words from this list.

insoluble **soluble** **solute** **solution** **solvent**

Nail varnish is ______________ in water. Water cannot be used to remove varnish from nails. Nail varnish is ______________ in nail varnish remover. [2 marks]

D–C

b A solute and a solvent that do not separate is a ______________. [1 mark]

Making crude oil useful

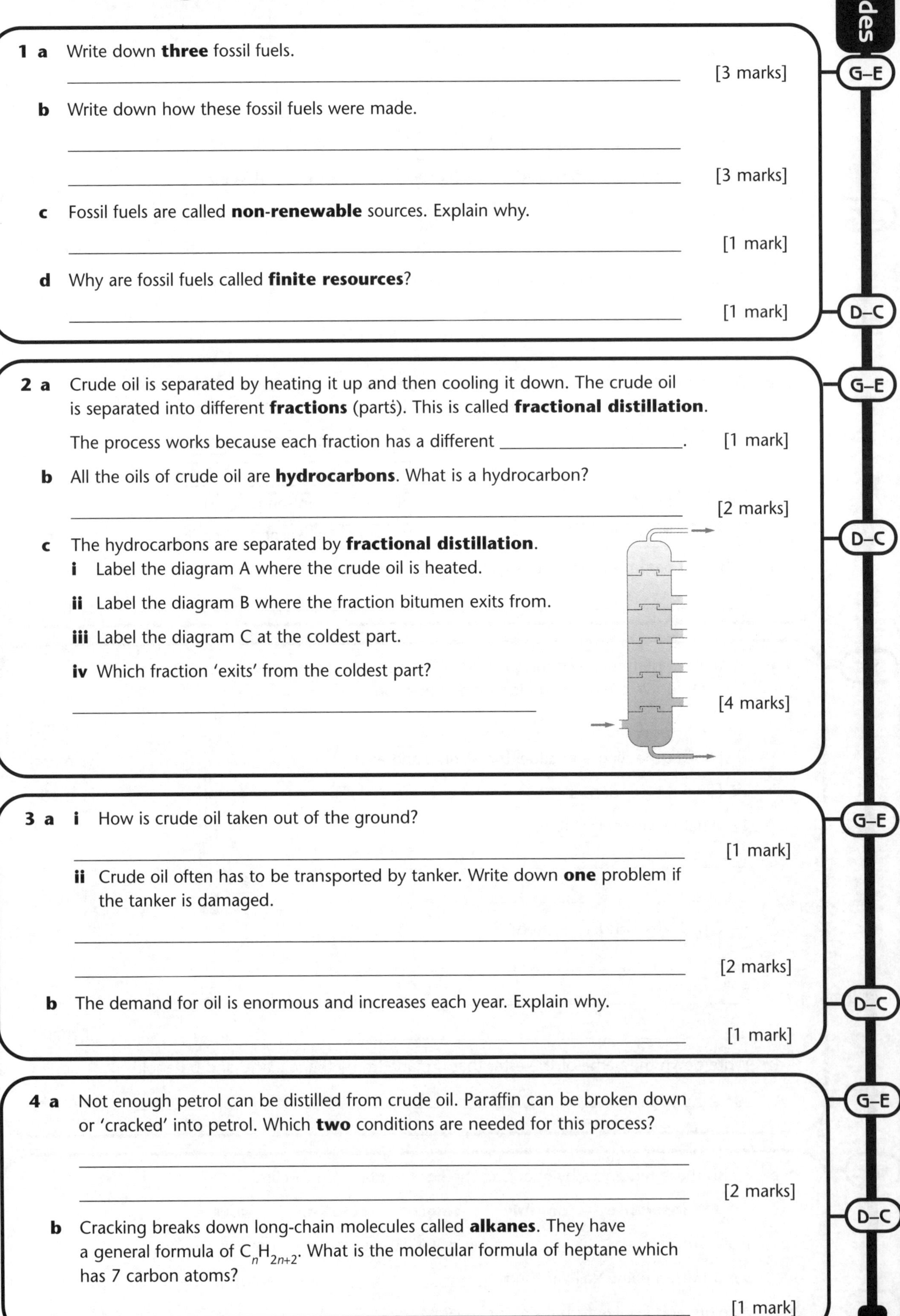

1 a Write down **three** fossil fuels.

____________________ [3 marks]

b Write down how these fossil fuels were made.

____

____________________ [3 marks]

c Fossil fuels are called **non-renewable** sources. Explain why.

____________________ [1 mark]

d Why are fossil fuels called **finite resources**?

____________________ [1 mark]

2 a Crude oil is separated by heating it up and then cooling it down. The crude oil is separated into different **fractions** (parts). This is called **fractional distillation**.

The process works because each fraction has a different ____________. [1 mark]

b All the oils of crude oil are **hydrocarbons**. What is a hydrocarbon?

____________________ [2 marks]

c The hydrocarbons are separated by **fractional distillation**.

i Label the diagram A where the crude oil is heated.

ii Label the diagram B where the fraction bitumen exits from.

iii Label the diagram C at the coldest part.

iv Which fraction 'exits' from the coldest part?

____________________ [4 marks]

3 a i How is crude oil taken out of the ground?

____________________ [1 mark]

ii Crude oil often has to be transported by tanker. Write down **one** problem if the tanker is damaged.

____

____________________ [2 marks]

b The demand for oil is enormous and increases each year. Explain why.

____________________ [1 mark]

4 a Not enough petrol can be distilled from crude oil. Paraffin can be broken down or 'cracked' into petrol. Which **two** conditions are needed for this process?

____

____________________ [2 marks]

b Cracking breaks down long-chain molecules called **alkanes**. They have a general formula of C_nH_{2n+2}. What is the molecular formula of heptane which has 7 carbon atoms?

____________________ [1 mark]

Making polymers

Grades

G–E

1 a Finish the sentences by choosing the **best** words from this list.

chains **monomers** **polymerisation** **polymers**

A plastic is made up of lots of ____________________ .

These are very big molecules made up of many small molecules joined together in ____________________ . The small molecules are called ____________________ . They join together. When lots of these are joined to make a big molecule the reaction is called ____________________ .

[4 marks]

D–C

b Which molecule is a polymer? Put a (ring) around **A**, **B**, **C** or **D**.

A

```
   H  H
   |  |
H—C—C—OH
   |  |
   H  H
```

B

```
   H  H  H
   |  |  |
H—C—C—C—H
   |  |  |
   H  H  H
```

C

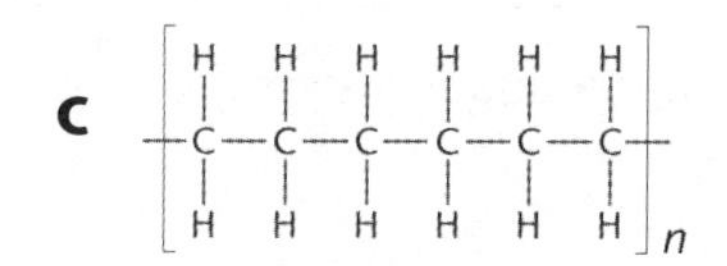

D

```
    H  H
    |  |
C—C=C—Cl
```

[1 mark]

c Write down **two** conditions needed for polymerisation.

____

____ [2 marks]

G–E

2 a Hydrocarbons are made up of ________________ and ________________. [1 mark]

b Which molecule is not a hydrocarbon, **A**, **B**, **C** or **D**? Put a (ring) around the correct answer.

A

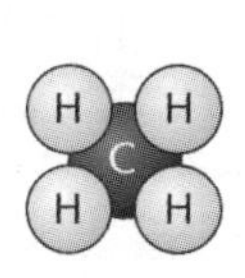

B

```
H   H
 \ /
  C
 / \
H   H
```

C

CH_4

D

```
   H  H  H
   |  |  |
H—C—C—C—Br
   |  |  |
   H  H  H
```

c i Look at the formula of propane.

```
   H  H  H
   |  |  |
H—C—C—C—H
   |  |  |
   H  H  H
```

It is an alkane. How do you know?

____ [1 mark]

ii What is the name of the alkene that has three carbon atoms?

____ [1 mark]

D–C

d i Butanol, C_4H_9OH

```
   H  H  H  H
   |  |  |  |
H—C—C—C—C—OH
   |  |  |  |
   H  H  H  H
```

is **not** a hydrocarbon. Explain why.

____ [1 mark]

ii Butene is an alkene.

```
   H  H  H  H
   |  |  |  |
H—C—C—C=C—H
   |  |  |
   H  H  H
```

Explain how you know.

____ [1 mark]

iii Butene is a **monomer**. What is **polybutene**?

____ [1 mark]

Designer polymers

Grades

G–E

1 a Write down **two uses** of polymers.

____

______________________________ [2 marks]

b Write down the **names** of **two** polymers.

____

______________________________ [2 marks]

c Each polymer is chosen carefully for the job that it does best. What kind of polymer do you need to cover electrical wires?

______________________________ [1 mark]

d There is a material used to make raincoats that is waterproof but 'breathable'. Why is this material better for raincoats than just a waterproof material?

______________________________ [1 mark]

D–C

e Nylon is tough, lightweight and keeps rainwater out but has a disadvantage. What is it?

______________________________ [1 mark]

f Suggest the properties that each polymer needs to have to be used for the purpose given. Finish the table.

polymer	property 1	property 2	use
PVC		flexible	raincoat
poly(ethene)	waterproof		plastic bags
poly(styrene)		absorbs shock	packaging
poly(propene)	strong		ropes

[4 marks]

G–E

2 a Most **addition polymers** are **non-biodegradable**. Explain what this means.

____

______________________________ [2 marks]

b Disposing of non-biodegradable polymers causes problems. Explain the problems for each of the ways of disposing.

Landfill sites ______________________________

____

Burning waste plastic ______________________________

____

Recycling ______________________________

____

D–C

c i Scientists are developing addition polymers that are **biodegradable**. Explain why.

____

______________________________ [2 marks]

ii Suggest a use for a biodegradable plastic.

______________________________ [1 mark]

Using carbon fuels

Grades

G–E

1 a Which is a good fuel for a car? Put a (ring) around the correct answer and then suggest why.

coal **petrol** **wood**

____

____ [2 marks]

characteristic	**coal**	**petrol**
energy value	high	high
availability	good	good
storage	bulky and dirty	volatile
toxicity	produces acid fumes	produces less acid fumes
pollution caused	acid rain, carbon dioxide and soot	carbon dioxide, nitrous oxides

D–C

b i Look at the table. Which fuel produces more acid fumes?

____ [1 mark]

ii Give **two** advantages of using either coal or petrol for heating.

____

____ [2 marks]

G–E

2 a Which gas is needed for fuels to burn?

____ [1 mark]

b Finish the sentence.

Combustion of a hydrocarbon fuel produces ______________________

and ______________________________________. [2 marks]

D–C

c Finish the sentences. Choose the **best** words from this list.

blue **less** **monoxide** **more** **soot** **toxic** **water vapour** **yellow**

If a fuel burns in a shortage of oxygen it gives off unwanted gases. One of the gases is carbon ____________ which is a ____________ gas and is very dangerous if it is breathed in. A Bunsen burner flame produces energy from burning gas. If the air hole is open a ____________ flame is seen. If the air hole is closed a ____________ flame is seen. Carbon ____________ , ____________ and ____________ are made and ____________ energy is transferred. [8 marks]

d i Write down a **word equation** for a hydrocarbon fuel burning in air.

____ [1 mark]

ii Write down the names of **two** products made in the complete combustion of a fuel.

____ [1 mark]

iii Describe how you would test for **one** of the products.

____

____ [2 marks]

Energy

Grades

G–E

1 a Finish the sentences. Choose the **best** words from this list.

electrical **energy** **heat** **light** **products** **reactants** **sound**

Chemical reactions can release energy such as ______________________ ,

______________________ , ______________________ or

______________________. [4 marks]

D–C

b Use the words **exothermic** and **endothermic** correctly in these sentences.

When energy is transferred **out** to the surroundings in a chemical reaction it is an

______________________ reaction (energy is released).

When energy is taken in from the surroundings in a chemical reaction it is an

______________________ reaction (absorbs energy).

An______________________ reaction is shown by a temperature **increase**.

Burning magnesium is an example of an ______________________ reaction. [4 marks]

G–E

2 a i Fuels need a gas to burn. Which gas?

______________________ [1 mark]

ii Ethanol burns to make carbon dioxide and water. Write down the word equation for this reaction.

______________________ [2 marks]

iii Write down the names of the **two reactants**.

______________________ [2 marks]

b i To compare the energy from two different fuels this apparatus is used twice. Label the **spirit burner**, **fuel**, **water** and **thermometer**. [4 marks]

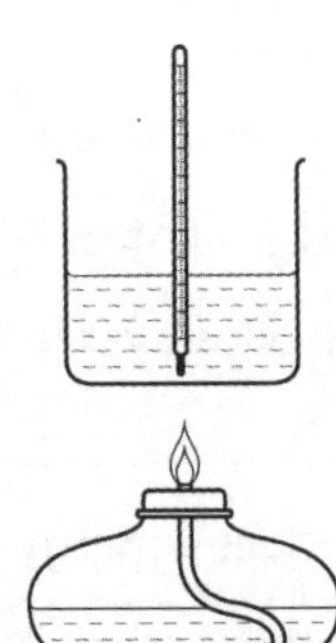

D–C

ii To compare the fuels, they are burned and the water is heated. Write down **three** measurements that need to be made.

____

______________________ [3 marks]

iii Write down **one** way that the experiment is made fair.

______________________ [1 mark]

C1 Revision checklist

- I know that cooking food is a chemical change as a new substance is made and it is an irreversible reaction. ☐
- I know that protein molecules in eggs and meat change shape when the food is cooked. ☐
- I know that the main food additives are antioxidants, food colours, emulsifiers and flavour enhancers. ☐
- I know that emulsifiers are molecules that have a water-loving part and an oil- or fat-loving part. ☐
- I know that alcohols react with acids to make an ester and water. ☐
- I know that a solute is the substance dissolved in a solvent to make a solution. ☐
- I know that crude oil is a non-renewable fossil fuel, which is a mixture of many hydrocarbons. ☐
- I know that petrol is a crude oil fraction with a low boiling point, which exits at the top of the fractional distillation tower. ☐
- I know that polymerisation is a process where many monomers react together to give a polymer. ☐
- I know that a hydrocarbon is a compound formed between carbon atoms and hydrogen atoms only. ☐
- I know that alkenes are hydrocarbons with one or more double bonds between carbon atoms. ☐
- I know that complete combustion of a hydrocarbon fuel makes carbon dioxide and water only. ☐
- I know that an exothermic reaction is one where energy is released into the surroundings. ☐
- I know that the energy of two fuels can be compared by the temperature rise in the same mass of water. ☐

Paints and pigments

Grades

G–E

1 a Write down **two** reasons why we use paints.

____

____ [2 marks]

b i Complete the sentence. Choose the **best** words from this list.

binding medium **colloid** **pigment** **solute** **solvent**

The three ingredients of paint are______________________,

______________________ and ______________________. [3 marks]

ii Oil paints are colloids. Explain why.

____

____ [2 marks]

D–C

c An **emulsion paint** is a water-based paint. Explain how it covers a surface.

____

____ [2 marks]

G–E

2 a Write down what happens to a thermochromic pigment when

i it gets hot ____

____ [1 mark]

ii it cools down ____

____ [1 mark]

b Another type of pigment takes in light energy during the day and gives out light energy at night. What is this pigment? Put a (ring) around the correct answer.

flammable **luminescent** **phosphorescent** **radiant**

D–C

c A thermochromic pigment changes colour at 45 °C. Write down **two** examples it is used for.

____

____ [2 marks]

G–E

3 a Dyes are used to colour fabrics. Some dyes are **natural**.
What are these made from?

____ [1 mark]

D–C

b Write down **two** ways that dyes made from chemicals are better than natural dyes.

____

____ [2 marks]

c We can now buy clothes in a much wider range of colours than our great-grandparents could. Explain why.

____

____

____ [3 marks]

Construction materials

Grades

G–E

1 a Write down **three** rocks that are used in construction.

____

____ [3 marks]

b Write down **two** metals that are used in construction.

____ [2 marks]

D–C

c Put these materials into the order of hardness.

granite **limestone** **marble**

Least hard ____________ ____________ ____________ Hardest [3 marks]

d Brick, concrete, steel, aluminium and glass are manufactured.
Finish the table to show the raw materials they come from.

building material	**brick**	**cement**	**glass**	**iron**	**aluminium**
raw material					

[5 marks]

G–E

2 There are environmental problems caused by taking rocks from the ground in a quarry.
Write down **three** problems.

____

____ [3 marks]

G–E

3 a Write down the names of **two** rocks that are forms of **calcium carbonate**.

____

____ [2 marks]

b Complete the sentence. Choose the **best** words from this list.

chemically electrolyses **insolubly precipitates** **thermally decomposes**

When calcium carbonate is heated, it ____________ ____________. [1 mark]

c Write down how concrete is made.

____

____

____ [4 marks]

d Why is concrete reinforced?

____ [1 mark]

D–C

e Reinforced concrete is a **composite** material. Explain why.

____ [2 marks]

f Calcium carbonate decomposes at a very high temperature. Write a word equation to show this.

____

____ [3 marks]

Does the Earth move?

G–E

1 a This is a diagram of the Earth.
Label the **iron core**, **mantle** and **crust**.

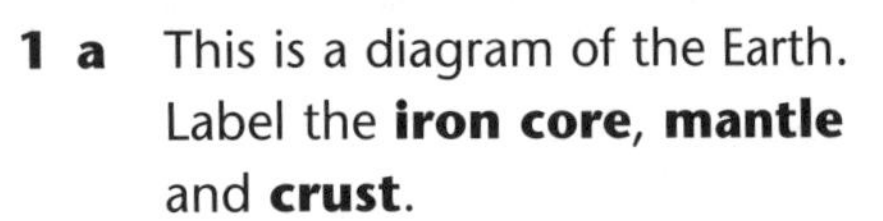

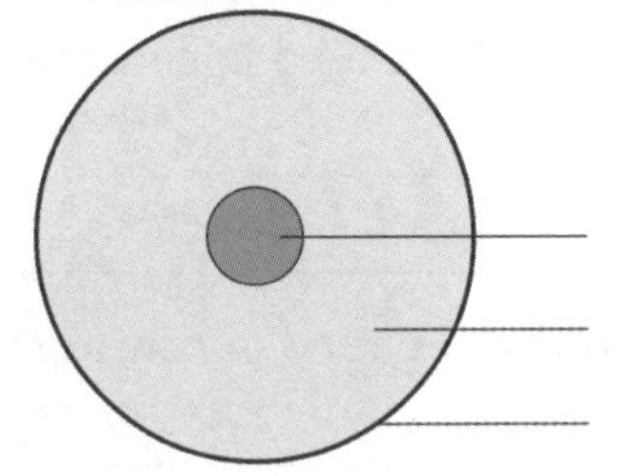

[3 marks]

b Sometimes the mantle comes through weaknesses in the Earth's crust.
What is the mantle made of?

______________________________ [1 mark]

c Finish the sentences. Choose the **best** words from this list.

earthquakes **iron** **rivers** **tectonic plates** **volcanoes**

The outer layer of the Earth is made of ______________________, which move very slowly over the molten rock. At the boundaries this movement causes ______________________ and ______________________. [3 marks]

D–C

d Are the tectonic plates that make up the Earth's crust less dense or more dense than the mantle?

______________________________ [1 mark]

e Write down the **two** kinds of tectonic plate.

______________________ and ______________________ [2 marks]

G–E

2 a i Magma slowly moves up to the surface of the Earth, cools down and solidifies to make which type of rock?

______________________________ [1 mark]

ii Some molten rock reaches the surface of the Earth and goes through weaknesses.

This is called ______________________. [1 mark]

iii This molten rock comes out in a **volcano**. Volcanoes can have runny or sticky molten rock. Which one is fairly safe and which is more dangerous? Explain why.

____

______________________________ [2 marks]

iv Why do most people think it is worth moving back to the area after a volcanic eruption?

______________________________ [2 marks]

D–C

b Magma can rise through the Earth's crust. Explain why.

______________________________ [1 mark]

c Magma cools and solidifies into igneous rock either after it comes out of a volcano as lava, or before it even gets to the surface. By looking at crystals of igneous rock, geologists can tell how quickly the rock cooled. Fill in the **two** boxes with an explanation and an example for each.

basalt **cools rapidly** **cools slowly** **granite**

small crystals

large crystals

[4 marks]

Metals and alloys

Grades

G–E

1 a Finish the sentences. Choose the **best** words from this list.

carbon **compound** **element** **oxygen** **nitrogen**

Rocks containing copper ore are mined. An ore is a ______________________.

Copper is a metal ______________________. In the laboratory copper is

extracted from its ore by heating it with ______________________. [3 marks]

b More than a third of all copper is recycled. Write down **two** reasons why.

____

______________________ [2 marks]

D–C

c Copper used for recycling has to be sorted carefully so that valuable 'pure' copper scrap is not mixed with less pure scrap. When impure copper is used to make alloys what must happen first?

______________________ [1 mark]

d If the scrap copper is very impure what must be done before it is used again?

______________________ [1 mark]

D–C

2 Impure copper can be purified in the laboratory using an electrolysis cell.

a What is the **anode** made from?

______________________ [1 mark]

b What happens at the **cathode**?

______________________ [1 mark]

G–E

3 a What is an **alloy**? ______________________ [1 mark]

b Examples of alloys are: amalgam, brass, bronze, solder and steel. Draw a **straight** line to match the use to the alloy.

amalgam	used to join metals
solder	used to make taps and door handles
brass	used by dentists to fill cavities in teeth

[3 marks]

D–C

c Most metals form alloys. Draw a **straight** line to match the metals to the alloy.

amalgam	contains copper and zinc
solder	contains mercury
brass	contains lead and tin

[3 marks]

d Alloys are often more useful than the original metals, though nowadays pure copper is more important than bronze or brass. Why are vast amounts turned into electric wire?

______________________ [1 mark]

Cars for scrap

Grades

G–E

1 a **Rust** is made when iron reacts with ________________ and ________________. [2 marks]

b In winter, icy roads are treated with salt. Why is this a problem for steel car bodies?

____ [1 mark]

D–C

c Aluminium does not corrode in moist air. Explain why.

____ [1 mark]

d Rust is an oxide layer but it does not protect the rest of the iron. Explain why.

____ [1 mark]

G–E

2 a Label the parts of the car that are made from four different materials: **metals**, **plastics**, **glass** and **fibres**.

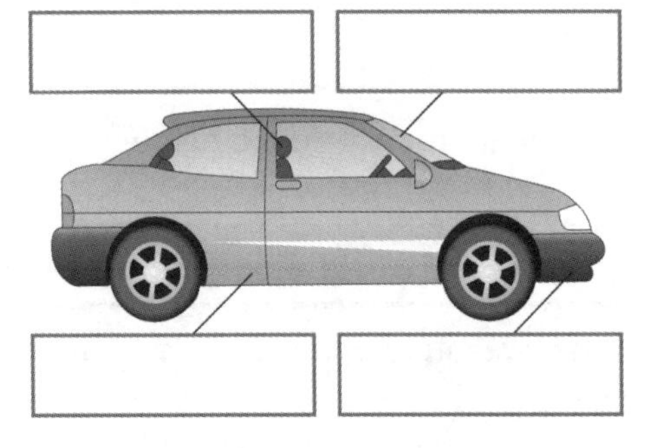

[4 marks]

b Draw a **straight** line to match the differences between iron and aluminium.

magnetic	iron
less dense	aluminium
corrodes easily	

[2 marks]

D–C

c **i** Finish the sentence. Steel is an alloy made of ________________ and ________________. [2 marks]

ii Write down **two** advantages of steel over iron.

____ [2 marks]

iii Steel and aluminium can both be used to make car bodies but each material has its own advantages. Write down **two** advantages of cars made from aluminium and **one** disadvantage.

____

____

____ [3 marks]

d Describe how the materials used in cars can be recycled at a scrap metal yard.

____ [1 mark]

D–C

3 Write down **three** benefits that recycling metals and the other materials of a car has on the environment.

____

____ [3 marks]

Clean air

Grades

G–E

1 a **Air** is a mixture of different gases. Write down the other **three** main gases.

		Water vapour	

[3 marks]

b Three processes change the levels of gases in the air. Draw a **straight** line to match up the processes.

increases the level of carbon dioxide and decreases the level of oxygen	combustion photosynthesis respiration	decreases the level of carbon dioxide and increases the level of oxygen

[3 marks]

D–C

c **i** Label the pie chart with the **four** main gases of the air in the correct section. [4 marks]

ii Mark in the percentages of the gases. [4 marks]

iii Explain how the carbon cycle keeps the balance between the percentage of carbon dioxide and oxygen in the atmosphere. Use your answer to question **1 b** to help you.

____

____

______________________________ [4 marks]

D–C

2 a Scientists know that gases trapped in liquid rock under the surface of the Earth are always escaping. Where does this happen?

______________________________ [1 mark]

b Scientists guess about the original atmosphere of the Earth. It's known that at some point in the Earth's history, microbes developed that could photosynthesise. Why were these important?

______________________________ [2 marks]

G–E

3 a **Pollutants** are substances made by human activity that harm the environment. The atmosphere contains a large number of pollutants. Finish the table.

D–C

pollutant	**carbon monoxide**	**oxides of nitrogen**	**sulfur dioxide**
environmental problem	*a poisonous gas*		
origin of pollutant		*formed in the internal combustion engine*	*formed when sulfur impurities in fossil fuels burn*

[3 marks]

b A car can be fitted with a **catalytic converter**. What does this do?

____

______________________________ [2 marks]

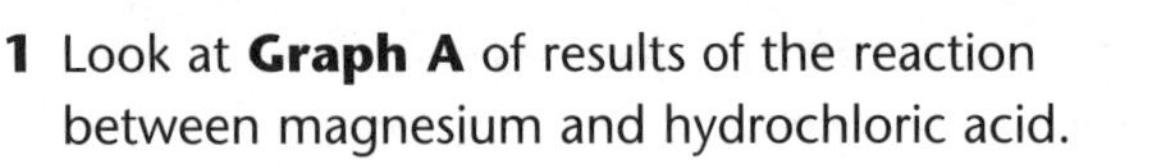

Faster or slower (1)

G–E

1 Look at **Graph A** of results of the reaction between magnesium and hydrochloric acid.

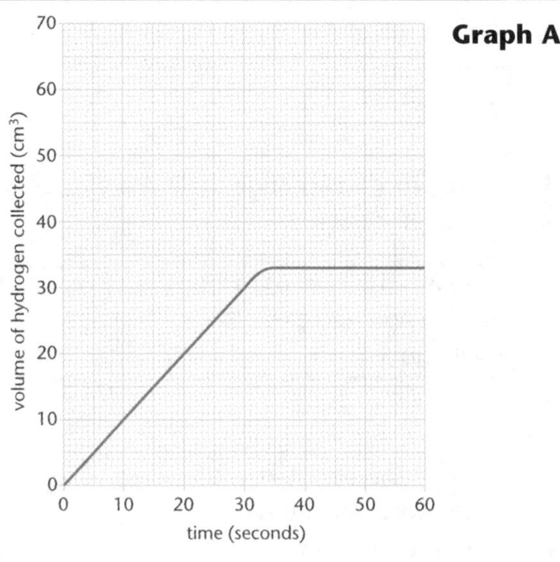

a At what time does the reaction stop?

____ [1 mark]

b Why does the reaction stop?

____ [1 mark]

c How much hydrogen was made at the end?

____ [1 mark]

G–E

2 Write down **two** ways that the speed of a reaction can be changed.

____

____ [2 marks]

D–C

3 Look at **Graph B**. It shows the reaction between magnesium and acid at 20 °C.

a If the reaction takes place at a higher temperature mark the reaction line that you would expect on the graph. Label this line **C**. [2 marks]

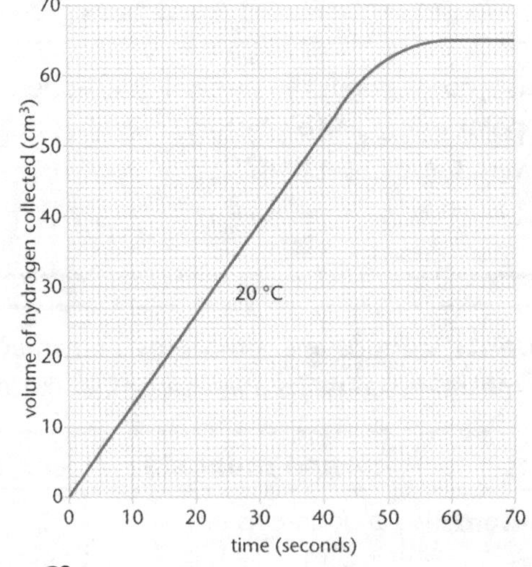

b Which graph has the steeper gradient, **B** or **C**?

____ [1 mark]

c The reaction rate increases at higher temperatures. Explain why. Use ideas about particles in your answer.

____

____

____ [4 marks]

Faster or slower (2)

Grades

G–E

1 a What is an explosion?

[1 mark]

b Write down **two** examples.

[2 marks]

D–C

c What products are made during an explosion?

[2 marks]

G–E

2 a If a reaction takes place with a powdered reactant or the same mass of a block of reactant, which will react faster? Use ideas about collisions between particles.

D–C

[3 marks]

b The reaction between calcium carbonate and hydrochloric acid is measured by the decrease in mass. Look at the equation. Why is there a decrease in mass?

$CaCO_3 + 2HCl \rightarrow CaCl_2 + H_2O + CO_2$

[2 marks]

c The graph shows how the rate of reaction between calcium carbonate and dilute hydrochloric acid is measured.

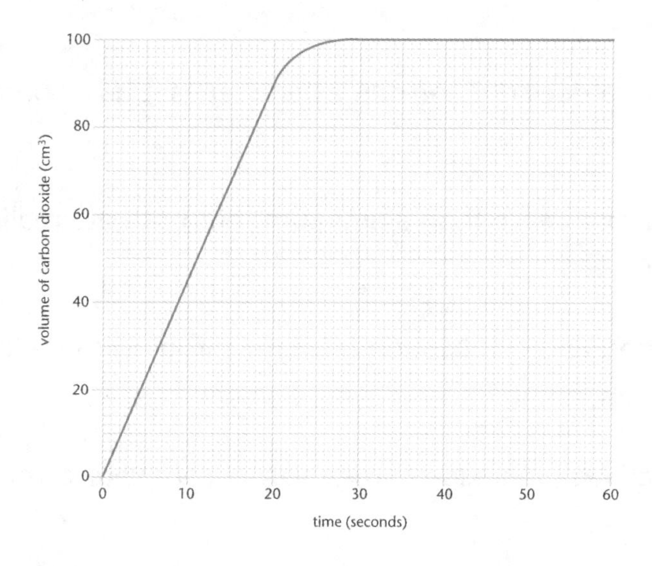

i At which time does the reaction stop? __________ [1 mark]

ii If this reaction used lumps of calcium carbonate, sketch on the graph the line that would show the reaction of the same mass of calcium carbonate as powder. [2 marks]

iii Why does the reaction speed up? Use ideas about collisions in your answer.

[1 mark]

G–E

3 a What is a catalyst?

[1 mark]

D–C

b A catalyst has two features. Describe them.

[2 marks]

C2 Revision checklist

- I know that paint is a colloid where solid particles are dispersed in a liquid, but are not dissolved.
- I know that thermochromic pigments change colour when heated or cooled.
- I know that brick is made from clay, glass from sand, and aluminium and iron from ores.
- I know that the equation for the decomposition of limestone is: calcium carbonate → calcium oxide + carbon dioxide
- I know that the outer layer of the Earth is continental plates with oceanic plates under oceans.
- I know that igneous rock is made when molten rock cools down.
- I know that copper can be extracted by heating its ore with carbon, but purified by electrolysis.
- I know that alloys often have properties that are different from the metals they are made from.
- I know that aluminium does not corrode when wet as it has a protective layer of aluminium oxide.
- I know that iron is more dense than aluminium, but both are malleable and electrical conductors.
- I know that respiration and combustion increase carbon dioxide levels and decrease oxygen levels.
- I know that toxic carbon monoxide comes from incomplete combustion of petrol or diesel in cars.
- I know that a temperature increase makes particles move faster, so increasing the rate of reaction.
- I know that a catalyst is a substance that changes the rate of reaction but is unchanged at the end.

Grades

What are atoms like?

G–E

1 a i This is a diagram of an atom. Label the nucleus and the electrons.

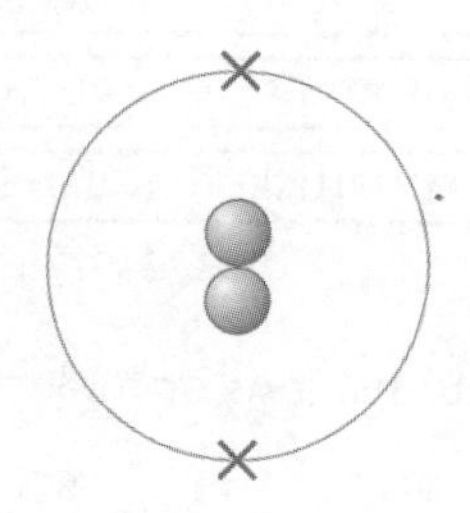

[3 marks]

ii Why is an atom neutral?

____ [1 mark]

D–C

b What are the particles in the nucleus of an atom?

____ [1 mark]

c Finish the table to show the relative mass and charge of the atomic particles.

	relative charge	**relative mass**
electron		0.0005 (zero)
proton	+1	
neutron		

[4 marks]

d What is the atomic number of an atom?

____ [1 mark]

e What is the mass number?

____ [1 mark]

G–E

2

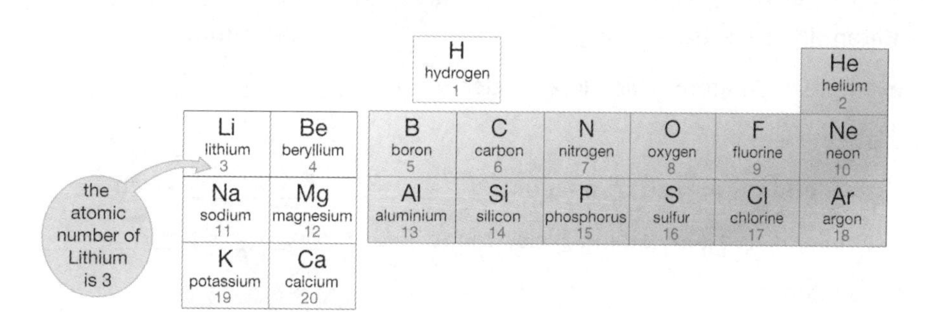

a What is the element of atomic number 15? ____________ [1 mark]

b What is the atomic number of the element calcium? ____________ [1 mark]

c What is an element?

____ [1 mark]

d How many elements are there in the periodic table? ____________ [1 mark]

e What is a compound?

____ [1 mark]

D–C

f What is an isotope?

____ [1 mark]

Ionic bonding

Grades

G–E

1 a Draw a **straight** line to match the word with the description.

atom — has more than one atom in its formula and no charge

molecule — is a charged atom or group of atoms

ion — is the smallest particle that can bond with another particle

[2 marks]

b Finish the table by writing these atoms, ions or molecules in the correct box.

O **Cl^-** **Mg** **H_2** **Na^+** **H** **SO_4^{2-}** **$MgSO_4$** **NaOH**

atom	ion	molecule

[3 marks]

D–C

2 a Put a tick (✓) in the box next to the sentence that describes a **metal** atom.

i An **atom** has extra electrons in its outer shell and needs to **lose** them to be stable. ☐

ii An atom has 'spaces' in its outer shell and needs to **gain** electrons to be stable. ☐

[1 mark]

b Draw a diagram to show how the electrons transfer from the metal atom to a non-metal atom to form a stable pair. **Outer shells only**.

[3 marks]

c Finish the sentences.

i If an atom loses electrons a ______________________ **ion** is formed. [1 mark]

ii An example of an atom which loses 1 electron is ______________________. [1 mark]

d Finish the sentences.

i A **negative ion** is formed by an atom ______________________ electrons. [1 mark]

ii An example of an atom gaining 1 electron is ______________________. [1 mark]

e Finish the sentences.

During **ionic bonding**, the metal atom becomes a ______________________

ion and the non-metal atom becomes a ______________________ ion.

The positive ion and the negative ion then attract one another. They attract to

a number of other ions to make a solid______________________. [3 marks]

G–E

3 a Sodium chloride and magnesium oxide have similar properties. Describe their melting points.

______________________ [1 mark]

D–C

b Put a tick (✓) in the boxes next to the substances that conduct electricity.

sodium chloride solution ☐ solid sodium chloride ☐

molten (melted) magnesium oxide ☐ solid magnesium oxide ☐

molten sodium chloride. ☐

[3 marks]

Covalent bonding

Grades

G–E

1 A molecule has the formula CO_2.

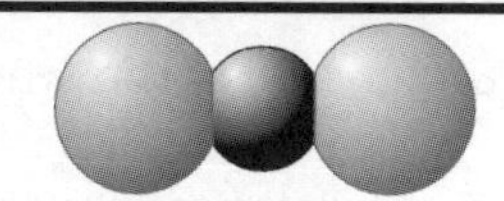

a How many atoms does it have altogether? ______________________ [1 mark]

b How many **different** atoms does it have? ______________________ [1 mark]

D–C

2 a Non-metals combine together by **sharing** electrons. What is this type of bonding?

______________________ [1 mark]

b Look at the diagram.

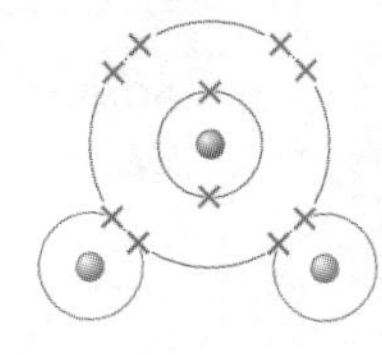

Explain how a water molecule is formed from atoms of other elements.

____

____

______________________ [4 marks]

c Carbon dioxide and water do not conduct electricity. Explain why.

______________________ [1 mark]

G–E

3 Look at the section of the periodic table.

		H hydrogen 1					He helium 2
Li lithium 3	Be beryllium 4	B boron 5	C carbon 6	N nitrogen 7	O oxygen 8	F fluorine 9	Ne neon 10
Na sodium 11	Mg magnesium 12	Al aluminium 13	Si silicon 14	P phosphorus 15	S sulfur 16	Cl chlorine 17	Ar argon 18
K potassium 19	Ca calcium 20						

a i Lithium is in a group. Which one? ______________________ [1 mark]

ii Write down two other elements in this group.

______________________ [2 marks]

b Three of these elements are in the same period. Put a (ring) around the correct answers.

oxygen **sodium** **silicon** **hydrogen** **sulphur** **potassium** [3 marks]

D–C

c Sodium is in group 1. Explain why.

______________________ [1 mark]

d Chlorine atoms have 7 electrons in the outer shell. In which group is chlorine?

______________________ [1 mark]

e i To which period does fluorine belong?

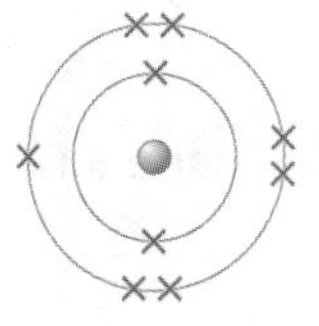

______________________ [1 mark]

ii Explain why.

______________________ [1 mark]

The group 1 elements

Grades

G–E

1 a Sodium and potassium are stored under oil. Explain why.

____

____ [2 marks]

b Lithium, sodium and potassium react with water.

i They float on the surface. Explain why.

____ [1 mark]

ii Which gas is given off?

____ [1 mark]

c Sodium reacts very vigorously with water and forms sodium hydroxide.
Write down the word equation for the reaction of sodium with water.

____ [2 marks]

D–C

d Finish the sentence about the order of reactivity of the alkali metals with water.

____________________ is more reactive than ____________________

which is more reactive than ____________________. [2 marks]

e Reactivity of the alkali metals with water increases down group 1.

reactivity increases down

	melting point in °C	**boiling point in °C**
$_{3}Li$	179	1317
$_{11}Na$	98	
$_{19}K$		774

Estimate the melting point of potassium ____________________ and

the boiling point of sodium ____________________. [2 marks]

f Group 1 metals have similar properties. Explain why.

____ [1 mark]

G–E

2 a Marie and Mitch have made some salts. They are salts of lithium, sodium and potassium. They have three labels to put on three bottles, but are not sure which one was the lithium salt. They decide to check with a flame test. Draw a **straight** line to match their results.

red	potassium
yellow	lithium
lilac	sodium

[2 marks]

D–C

b How did Marie and Mitch carry out their experiment?

____

____

____

____ [4 marks]

The group 7 elements

G–E

1 a Group 7 elements are called the halogens. Write down their uses.

i Chlorine ____________________ [1 mark]

ii Iodine ____________________ [1 mark]

b Write down **two** uses of sodium chloride.

____

____________________ [2 marks]

D–C

2 a There is a **trend** in the physical appearance of the halogens at room temperature. Finish the table.

chlorine	
bromine	*orange liquid*
iodine	

[2 marks]

b Group 7 elements have similar properties. Explain why.

____________________ [1 mark]

c There is a trend in the reactivity of halogens.
Draw an arrow to show the trend of reactivity from the least reactive element towards the most reactive element.

Reactivity

$_{9}F$
$_{17}Cl$
$_{35}Br$
$_{53}I$

[1 mark]

d When a halogen reacts with an alkali metal a **metal halide** is made. Write down the word equation for the reaction between potassium and iodine.

____________________ [2 marks]

D–C

3 a If halogens are bubbled through **solutions of metal halides** there are two possibilities: **no reaction**, or a **displacement reaction**.

i If chlorine is bubbled through potassium bromide solution, a red-brown colour is seen. Explain why.

____________________ [1 mark]

ii If bromine is bubbled through potassium chloride solution there is no reaction. Explain why.

____________________ [1 mark]

b Bromine (Br_2) displaces iodine from potassium iodide solution (KI).

i Write down a word equation for this reaction.

____________________ [2 marks]

ii Write down a balanced symbol equation for this reaction.

____________________ [2 marks]

Electrolysis

Grades

G–E

1 a Finish the sentences by choosing the **best** words from this list. You may use any word more than once.

anode **cathode** **electrolysis** **electrolyte** **negative** **positive**

The decomposition of a liquid by using electricity is called ____________________.

The ____________________ is a liquid that conducts electricity. There are two electrodes called the ____________________ and the ____________________.

The ____________________ is the positive electrode and the ____________________ is the negative electrode.

During electrolysis the ____________________ ions are attracted to the anode and the are ____________________ ions attracted to the cathode. [8 marks]

D–C

2 a Explain the key features of the electrolysis of dilute sulfuric acid.

____

____

____

____

____________________ [6 marks]

b Explain why the volume of hydrogen gas and the volume of oxygen gas given off in this process are different.

____________________ [1 mark]

G–E

3 The two gases given off during the electrolysis of sulfuric acid can be tested.

a Describe the test for hydrogen.

____

____________________ [2 marks]

b Describe the test for oxygen.

____

____________________ [2 marks]

D–C

4 a Write about the key features of the production of aluminium by electrolytic decomposition.

____

____

____

____________________ [4 marks]

b Write down the word equation for the decomposition of aluminium oxide.

____________________ [1 mark]

Transition elements

G–E

1 a Transition elements have typical metallic properties. Write down **six** properties.

____

____

____

____

____

______________________ [6 marks]

D–C

b A compound that contains a transition element is often coloured.

i What is the colour of copper compounds?

____

ii What is the colour of iron(II) compounds?

____

iii What is the colour of iron(III) compounds?

______________________ [3 marks]

c A transition metal and its compounds are often catalysts.

i Which transition metal is used in the Haber process to produce ammonia?

______________________ [1 mark]

ii If the metal used to harden margarine is number 28, suggest whether this is a transition metal or not. Use the periodic table on page 238 to help you.

______________________ [1 mark]

G–E

2 When a yellow solution of potassium chromate is added to a colourless solution of silver nitrate a yellow solid is formed. What is this type of reaction called?

______________________ [1 mark]

D–C

3 a In a reaction a substance is broken down into at least **two** other substances by heat. What is this type of reaction?

______________________ [1 mark]

b If a transition metal carbonate is heated it decomposes to form a metal oxide and carbon dioxide. Write down the word equation for the decomposition of copper carbonate.

______________________ [1 mark]

D–C

4 Sodium hydroxide solution is used to identify the presence of transition metal ions in solution. Finish the table.

ion	colour
Cu^{2+}	
Fe^{2+}	
Fe^{3+}	

[3 marks]

Metal structure and properties

Grades

G–E

1 a Look at the table.

	property						
metal	**lustre**	**hardness**	**density**	**heat conductor**	**electrical conductor**	**melting point**	**boiling point**
A	yes	high	high	high	high	high	high
B	no	high	high	high	high	high	high
C	yes	low	high	high	high	lower	lower

i Which metal is not as hard as the others? ________________ [1 mark]

ii Which metal is not as shiny (lustrous) as the others? ________________ [1 mark]

iii Which metal has the lowest boiling point? ________________ [1 mark]

b The uses of a metal depend on its properties.
Which metal, **A**, **B** or **C**, would be best to make a ring or other jewellery? _______ [1 mark]

D–C

c Silver is often chosen to make a piece of jewellery. Which **two** properties does it have that are important for this? Choose words from this list.

ductile **good electrical conductor** **high boiling point**
high melting point **lustrous** **malleable**
good thermal conductivity

____ [2 marks]

d Copper is often used for the base or the whole of a saucepan. Use your knowledge about chemical properties to explain why.

____

____

____ [3 marks]

G–E

2 a In the box draw how the atoms of a metal form a structure.

[1 mark]

b Write down **two** ways that you know this is the structure of a metal not a liquid.

____ [2 marks]

G–E

3 a What condition is needed for some metals to become **superconductors**?

____ [1 mark]

D–C

b What are superconductors?

____ [1 mark]

c What are **three** potential benefits of superconductors?

____

____

____ [3 marks]

C3 Revision checklist

- I know that the nucleus is made up of protons and neutrons, with each having a relative mass of 1. ☐
- I know that electrons surround the nucleus and occupy shells in order. They have almost no mass, 0. ☐
- I know that positive ions are formed by the loss of electrons from the outer shell. ☐
- I know that negative ions are formed by the gain of electrons into the outer shell. ☐
- I can work out the number of each different type of atom in a molecule or displayed formula. ☐
- I know that there are two types of bonding – ionic bonding and covalent bonding. ☐
- I know that lithium, sodium and potassium react vigorously with water and give off hydrogen. ☐
- I know that group 1 metals have one electron in their outer shell, which is why they are similar. ☐
- I know that chlorine is a green gas, bromine is an orange liquid and iodine is a grey solid. ☐
- I know that chlorine is more reactive than bromine, which is more reactive than iodine. ☐
- I know that in the electrolysis of dilute sulphuric acid, H_2 is made at the cathode and O_2 at the anode. ☐
- I know that when aluminium oxide is electrolysed, Al is formed at the cathode and O_2 at the anode. ☐
- I know that compounds of copper are blue, iron(II) are light green and iron(III) are orange/brown. ☐
- I know that metals have particles which are arranged close together in a regular arrangement. ☐

Acids and bases

Grades

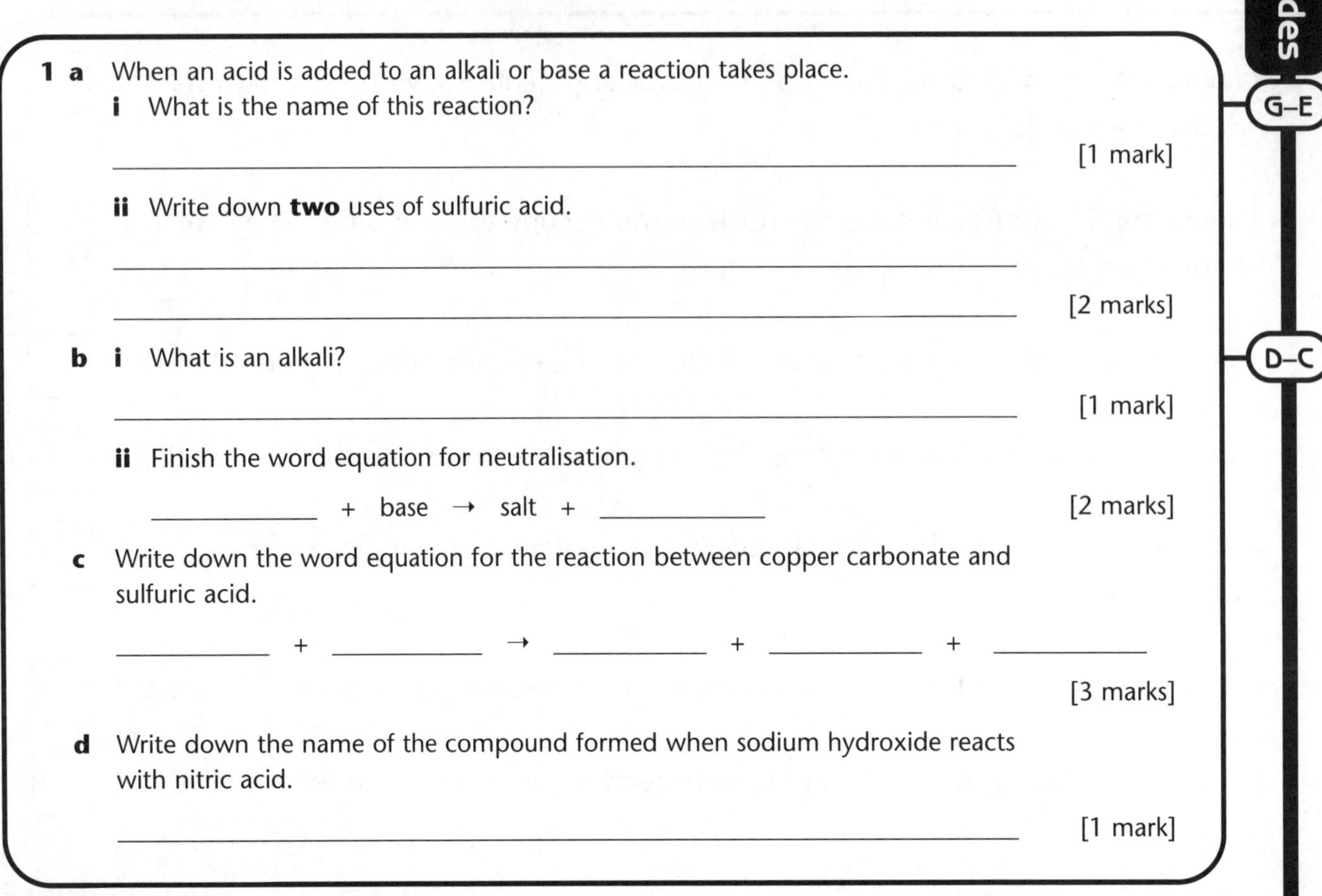

G–E

1 a When an acid is added to an alkali or base a reaction takes place.

i What is the name of this reaction?

______________________________ [1 mark]

ii Write down **two** uses of sulfuric acid.

____

______________________________ [2 marks]

D–C

b i What is an alkali?

______________________________ [1 mark]

ii Finish the word equation for neutralisation.

__________ + base → salt + __________ [2 marks]

c Write down the word equation for the reaction between copper carbonate and sulfuric acid.

__________ + __________ → __________ + __________ + __________

[3 marks]

d Write down the name of the compound formed when sodium hydroxide reacts with nitric acid.

______________________________ [1 mark]

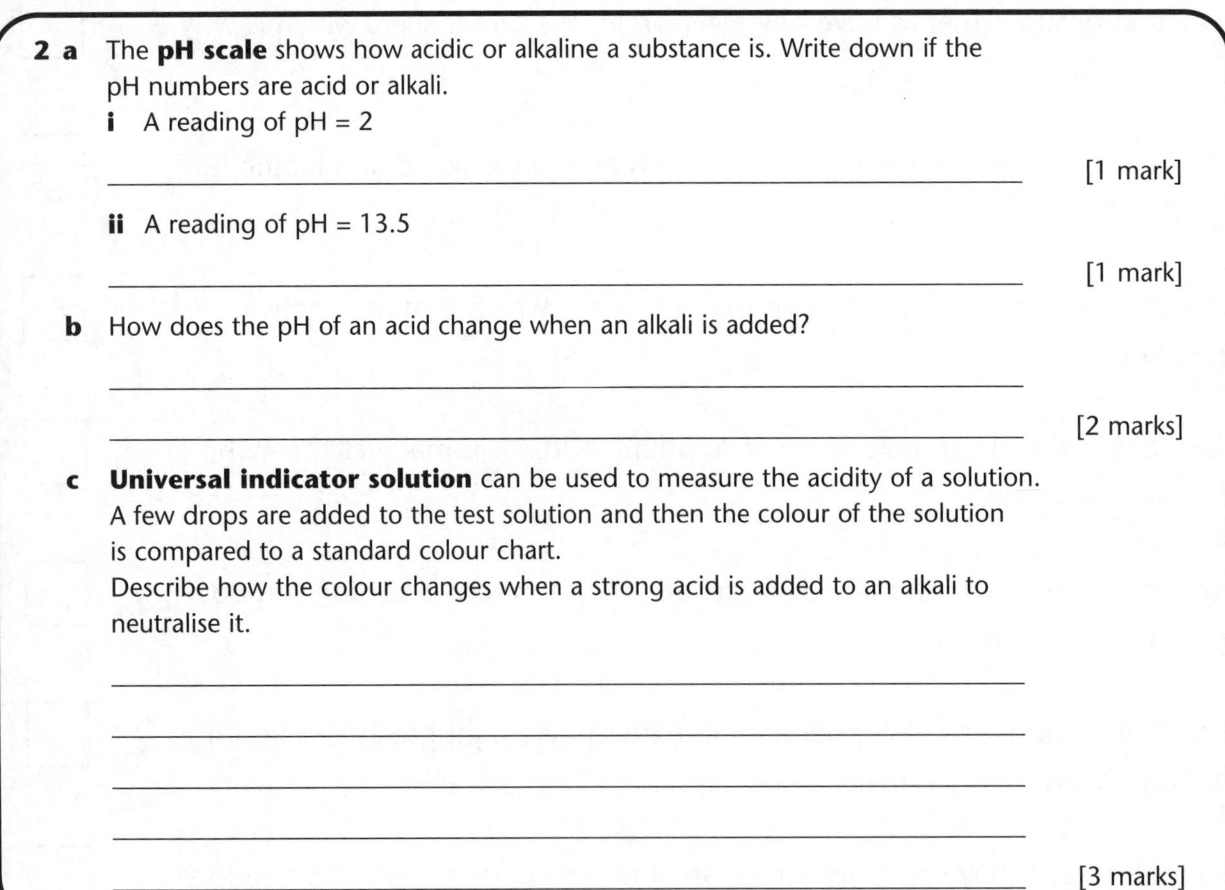

G–E

2 a The **pH scale** shows how acidic or alkaline a substance is. Write down if the pH numbers are acid or alkali.

i A reading of pH = 2

______________________________ [1 mark]

ii A reading of pH = 13.5

______________________________ [1 mark]

b How does the pH of an acid change when an alkali is added?

____

______________________________ [2 marks]

D–C

c **Universal indicator solution** can be used to measure the acidity of a solution. A few drops are added to the test solution and then the colour of the solution is compared to a standard colour chart.
Describe how the colour changes when a strong acid is added to an alkali to neutralise it.

____

____

____

____

______________________________ [3 marks]

Grades

Reacting masses

G–E

1 a Look at the periodic table on page 4.

i Find the relative atomic mass of iron, Fe. ______________ [1 mark]

ii Work out the relative formula mass of NaOH.

______________ [1 mark]

iii Work out the relative formula mass of $CaCO_3$.

______________ [1 mark]

b Work out the relative formula mass of $Ca(OH)_2$.
Use the relative atomic masses.

H 1 C 12 O 16 Na 23 Ca 40

______________ [1 mark]

c The total mass in a reaction never changes. The mass of the **products** is exactly the same as the mass of the reactants. However, if the mass of the reacting chemicals goes down there is a reason.

i Write down a possible reason for the total mass in a reaction going down.

______________ [1 mark]

ii Write down a possible reason for the mass of a burning reactant going up.

______________ [1 mark]

d Sometimes a reaction does not give as much chemical as it should. Some chemicals always get left behind, so the amount of product that is collected is usually less than the amount that was expected. Suggest **two** ways the product is lost.

____

____

______________ [2 marks]

2 Leo and Lesley made some crystals of magnesium sulphate. They did not make as much as they hoped. They wanted to make 42 g. They only made 28 g.

a What was their 'actual yield'?

______________ [1 mark]

b What was their 'predicted yield'?

______________ [1 mark]

c How will they calculate their percentage yield?

____

______________ [1 mark]

d What was their percentage yield?

____

______________ [2 marks]

Fertilisers and crop yield

Grades

G–E

1 a Plants need carbon dioxide and water. They also need essential elements. How do they get these?

______________________________ [1 mark]

b What are the essential elements that help plants grow bigger and faster?

______________________________ [3 marks]

c These essential elements are found naturally in the ground. What can be added to increase the amount needed for plants to grow bigger?

______________________________ [1 mark]

D–C

d Why do farmers add fertilisers?

______________________________ [1 mark]

e How do fertilisers get into the plants?

______________________________ [1 mark]

f To calculate the yield when making a fertiliser you need to calculate its **relative formula mass**. What is the relative formula mass of ammonium sulphate $(NH_4)_2SO_4$? Use the periodic table on page 4.

______________________________ [2 marks]

G–E

2 a This is the apparatus needed to make a fertiliser from an acid and an alkali.

A

evaporating basin

crystals begin to form

B

C

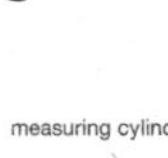
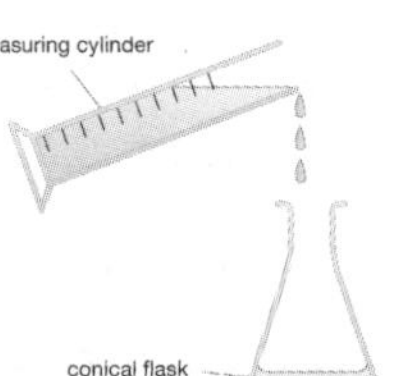

D

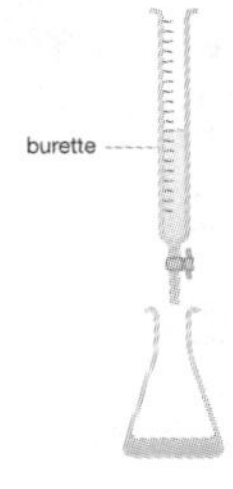

The pictures are in the wrong order. Write the letters of the pictures in the right order.

______________________________ [1 mark]

b Describe what is happening at each stage.

A ______________________________ [1 mark]

B ______________________________ [1 mark]

C ______________________________ [1 mark]

D ______________________________ [1 mark]

D–C

c Many fertilisers are **salts**, so they can be made by reacting acids with bases. What else is made?

acid + base → salt + ______________ [1 mark]

d Don and Demi want to make some ammonium phosphate.

i Which acid will they need to use? ______________________________ [1 mark]

ii Which alkali will they need to use? ______________________________ [1 mark]

iii Write down a word equation to show this reaction.

______________________________ [2 marks]

The Haber process

G–E

1 a Write down the name of the chemical made by joining nitrogen and hydrogen in the Haber process.

______________________________ [1 mark]

b Where does the nitrogen for this process come from?

______________________________ [1 mark]

c What does the sign $\rightleftharpoons$ mean?

______________________________ [1 mark]

D–C

2 Write about how ammonia is made. Include the conditions needed in your answer.

____

____

______________________________ [3 marks]

G–E

3 a Write down **three** things that affect the cost of making the ammonia.

____

____

______________________________ [3 marks]

D–C

b For the factors you have chosen above, explain why they affect the cost of making a new substance.

factor	explanation

[3 marks]

c Look at the graph.
At which pressure is most ammonia made at 400 °C ?

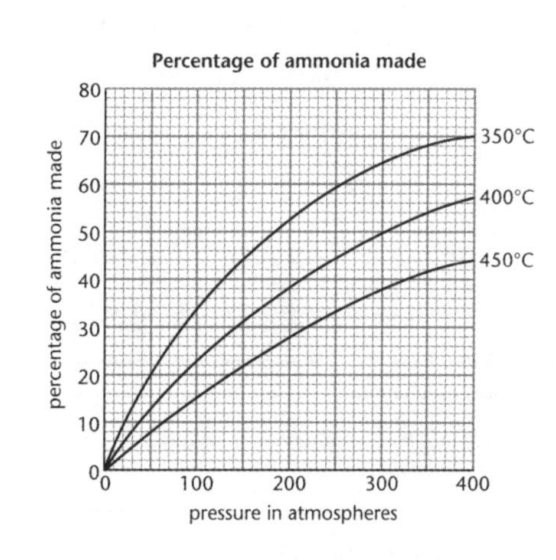

______________________________ [1 mark]

d As the pressure increases what happens to the yield of ammonia?

______________________________ [1 mark]

e As the temperature increases what happens to the yield of ammonia?

______________________________ [1 mark]

Detergents

Grades

G–E

1 a Draw a **straight** line to match the ingredients in detergents with their action.

Ingredient	Action
active detergent	to soften hard water
water softener	to give a whiter than white appearance
bleaches	to remove food stains at low temperatures
optical brighteners	to do the cleaning
enzymes	to remove coloured stains

[4 marks]

D–C

b A detergent can be made by **neutralising** an organic acid using an alkali. Write a word equation for this reaction.

______________________________ [2 marks]

c Why are detergents used to clean greasy plates?

____

______________________________ [2 marks]

d New washing powders allow clothes to be washed at low temperatures.

i This is good for the environment. Explain why.

____

______________________________ [2 marks]

ii It is also good for coloured clothes to be washed at low temperatures. Explain why.

____

______________________________ [2 marks]

G–E

2 Finish the sentences. Choose the **best** words from this list.

solution **soluble** **solute** **insoluble** **solvents**

We need to dissolve blue ink. Methylated spirit and water are both ______________.

They dissolve other substances. The blue ink is the substance that dissolves.

Blue ink is the ______________. Blue ink dissolved in a solvent makes a

______________.

Different solvents dissolve different substances. If a substance dissolves,

it is ______________. If it does not dissolve, it is ______________. [5 marks]

D–C

3 a Some fabrics will be damaged if they are washed in water. How are they cleaned?

______________________________ [1 mark]

b Machines are used to wash clothes in an organic solvent. Why is the solvent used called 'dry'?

______________________________ [1 mark]

Batch or continuous?

Grades

G–E

1 a There are two types of processes, **batch** and **continuous**.

i Which type of chemical is made by a batch process?

____ [1 mark]

ii Which type of chemical is made by a continuous process?

____ [1 mark]

D–C

b Why are pharmaceuticals made in small batches?

____ [1 mark]

c How is the large scale production of ammonia different from the small scale production of pharmaceuticals?

____ [1 mark]

G–E

2 a The raw materials for a medicine can be made synthetically. Write down another way these raw materials can be found.

____ [1 mark]

D–C

b Explain the steps needed.

____

____

____

____ [4 marks]

G–E

3 a Write down **three** factors that affect the cost of making and developing a medicine.

____

____

____ [3 marks]

D–C

b Draw **straight** lines to match the reasons for the high costs of making and developing medicine and pharmaceutical drugs to the **best** explanation.

strict safety laws	The medicines are made by a batch process so less automation can be used.
research and development	They may be rare and costly
raw materials	They take years to develop
labour intensive	People need to be feel a benefit without too many side effects

[3 marks]

Nanochemistry

Grades

1 a Finish the table to show the properties and uses of these three forms of carbon.

G–E

	diamond	**graphite**	**buckminster fullerene**
appearance		*black solid*	
solubility	*insoluble in water*	*insoluble in water*	*deep red solution in petrol*
electrical conductivity	*does not conduct electricity*		
uses			*can join together to make nanotubes*
reasons for use			

[9 marks]

b Draw a **straight** line to match the carbon to its correct structure.

D–C

carbon	**structure**
diamond	
graphite	
buckminster fullerene	

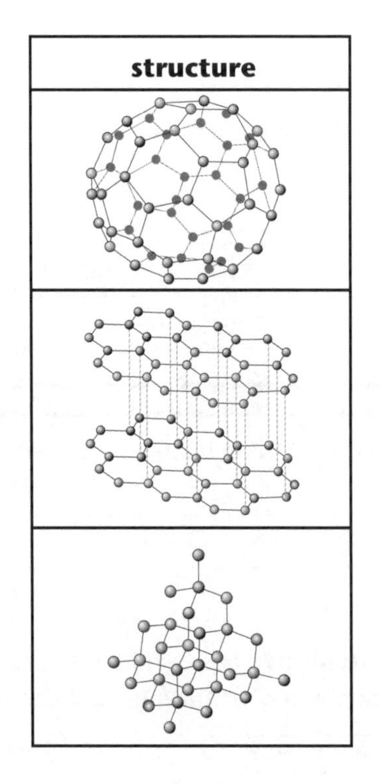

[3 marks]

2 a Fullerenes are black solids that dissolve in petrol. What colour solution do they make?

G–E

___ [1 mark]

b Fullerenes can join together to make nanotubes.

i Write down **two** properties of nanotubes.

___

___ [2 marks]

D–C

ii Write down **two** uses of nanotubes.

___

___ [2 marks]

How pure is our water?

Grades

G–E

1 a Write down **four** places where large amounts of water are found in the United Kingdom.

____

____

____

______________________________ [4 marks]

b Write down **two** ways that water is used by industry.

______________________________ [2 marks]

c Write down **two** things that are in water before it is purified.

______________________________ [2 marks]

d Write down **two** pollutants found in drinking water.

______________________________ [2 marks]

D–C

e Explain why relief organisations concentrate on providing clean water supplies.

______________________________ [1 mark]

D–C

2 The water in a river is cloudy and often not fit to drink. To make clean drinking water it is passed through a **water purification** works.
Label the **three** main parts of this process. Explain what happens at each stage.

[________] → [________] → [________]

____

____

____

____

____

______________________________ [6 marks]

G–E

3 a Water may contain sulphate ions or halide ions. Precipitation reactions are used for testing water. Martin and Mariella tested for **chloride**, **bromide** and **iodide ions**. They added two drops of **silver nitrate** solution to the water in a test tube.
Finish their results table.

chlorides	
bromides	*cream precipitate*
iodides	

[2 marks]

b Which chemical do they add to test for sulfate ions? It gives a white precipitate.

______________________________ [1 mark]

D–C

c Write a word equation for the precipitation reaction between lead nitrate and potassium chloride.

______________________________ [2 marks]

C4 Revision checklist

- I know that solutions with a pH of less than 7 are acids, more than 7 are alkalis, but pH 7 is neutral. ☐
- I know that neutralisation is a reaction where: acid + base $\rightarrow$ salt + water. ☐
- I can work out the relative formula mass of a substance from its formula e.g. CO_2 is $12 + (2 \times 16) = 44$. ☐
- I can work out the percentage yield using the formula: % yield = actual yield $\times$ 100 $\div$ predicted yield. ☐
- I know that fertilisers provide extra nitrogen, phosphorus and potassium, essential for plant growth. ☐
- I know that ammonia is made by the Haber process where N_2 and H_2 are put over an iron catalyst. ☐
- I know that the higher the pressure, the higher the energy bill for the industrial plant. ☐
- I know that a catalyst will reduce costs as the rate of reaction is increased. ☐
- I know that solutes are soluble and dissolve in solvents to make solutions. ☐
- I know that dry cleaning is a process used to clean clothes using a solvent that is not water. ☐
- I know that a continuous process makes chemicals all the time but a batch process does not. ☐
- I can recognise the three structures of carbon: diamond, graphite and buckminster fullerene. ☐
- I can explain that graphite is slippery and is used as electrodes as it conducts electricity. ☐
- I know that water purification includes filtration, sedimentation and chlorination. ☐

Moles and empirical formulae

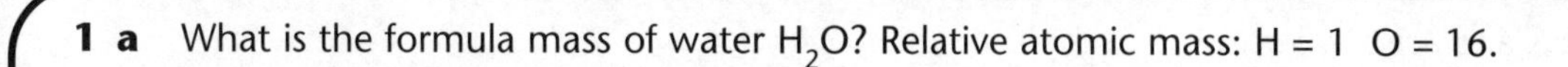

G–E

1 a What is the formula mass of water H_2O? Relative atomic mass: H = 1 O = 16.

______________________________ [1 mark]

Use the relative atomic mass of the elements below to answer the questions.

H = 1 O = 16 K = 39 N = 14 S = 32 C = 12 Zn = 65 Na = 23 Mg = 12

b Calculate the molar mass of KNO_3.

______________________________ [1 mark]

D–C

c Calculate the molar mass of $(NH_4)_2SO_4$.

______________________________ [2 marks]

G–E

2 a Nadine and Keiko heat 1.25 g zinc carbonate. They get 0.81 g zinc oxide.

Nadine says that the mass has 'disappeared'.

Keiko says that the mass lost is the same as the mass of a gas given off.

Who is correct? Remember why and write down your idea.

______________________________ [1 mark]

b Work out how much gas Keiko thought was given off.

______________________________ [1 mark]

D–C

c Nadine writes an equation.

$ZnCO_3 \rightarrow ZnO + CO_2$

The molar mass of $ZnCO_3$ is 125 g. The molar mass of ZnO is 81 g.

If she heats 2.5 g of $ZnCO_3$, how much ZnO will she get?

____

______________________________ [2 marks]

G–E

3 a If 2.4 g of magnesium is heated it should react with 3.2 g of oxygen.

How much magnesium oxide should be made?

______________________________ [1 mark]

D–C

b If 12 g of C reacts with oxygen to make 44 g of carbon dioxide, how much oxygen is used?

______________________________ [1 mark]

c How much Na is present in 8.5 g of $NaNO_3$ if there is 1.4 g N and 4.8 g oxygen?

____

______________________________ [2 marks]

D–C

4 a What is an empirical formula?

______________________________ [1 mark]

b What is the empirical formula of ethanoic acid CH_3COOH?

______________________________ [1 mark]

Electrolysis

Grades

1 a i Lukas and Anya want to electrolyse a solution of potassium nitrate. They choose this apparatus. Label the anode, cathode and DC power supply.

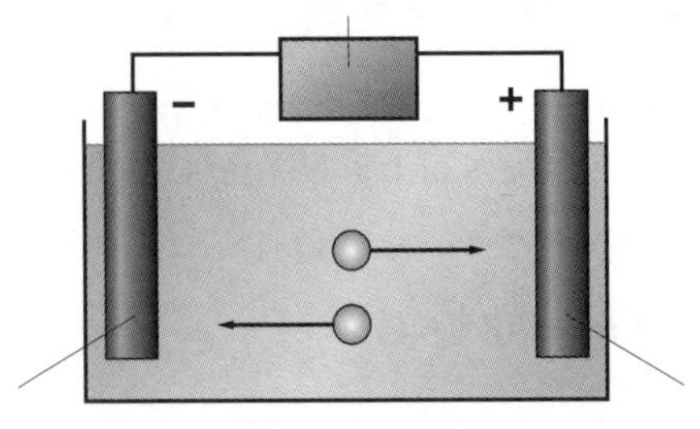

G–E

[3 marks]

ii The two circles represent ions. They each have a different charge.

Show which is the positive ion (+) and which is the negative ion (-). Write the signs in the circles. [1 mark]

b Lukas says that electrolysis is the decomposition of a liquid by passing an electric current through it. Anya says there is a more detailed explanation. What does she say?

D–C

______________________________ [2 marks]

c They electrolyse the solution of potassium nitrate in water. They collect two gases, one at each electrode. Which two gases?

______________ and ______________ [2 marks]

2 Lukas and Ben electrolyse copper sulfate. They use copper electrodes. They find the mass of the electrodes before and after the electrolysis.

a i What do they notice about the change in mass of the negative electrode?

D–C

______________________________ [1 mark]

ii What do they notice about the change in mass of the positive electrode?

______________________________ [1 mark]

b Lukas says that if they leave the electrolysis for longer they will get more copper.

Ben says if they increase the current they will get more copper.

Who is correct? Put a (ring) round the correct answer.

Ben **Both** **Lukas** **Neither** [1 mark]

3 a Anya and Jenny want to electrolyse some molten electrolytes.

D–C

Their teacher says this is difficult for them to do because the electrolytes have to be heated to a high temperature to melt them. Why do the electrolytes need to be melted?

______________________________ [2 marks]

b The teacher asked Anya and Jenny to predict what they would get at each electrode with these molten electrolytes. Complete their table.

G–E

molten electrolyte	at the cathode	at the anode
Al_2O_3		
$PbBr_2$		
PbI_2		
KCl		

[4 marks]

Quantitative analysis

1 Sean and Mary wanted to eat some pie. They look on the label.

	Pie per 100 g	% RDA
Energy	860 kJ	10%
Protein	5.0	
Carbohydrate:	19.0 g	
of which sugar	2.7 g	3%
Fat	12.2 g	17%
of which saturates	5.0 g	25%
of which unsaturates	7.2 g	
Fibre	1.0 g	
Sodium	0.1 g	
Sodium equivalent	0.3 g	5%

G–E

a How much fat does 100 g of pie have?

_______________ [1 mark]

b If they eat 200 g of pie, how much saturated fat would they eat?

_______________ [1 mark]

c If they eat 200 g of pie, what percentage of their RDA (recommended daily allowance) of saturated fat will they eat?

_______________ [1 mark]

D–C

d Sean suggests that they only eat 100 g of pie each. Suggest why he says this.

_______________ [2 marks]

G–E

2 a A milk carton holds 1 dm^3. How many cm^3 is this?

_______________ [1 mark]

b Mary finds that a squash bottle holds 750 cm^3. How many dm^3 is this?

_______________ [1 mark]

D–C

c The squash is too concentrated to drink. It has 15 g/dm^3. She pours 10 cm^3 of it into a glass.

How much water must Mary add to make it into a 5 g/dm^3 solution?

_______________ [1 mark]

3 It is important to dilute some concentrated liquids to the correct concentration.

G–E

a Write about an example of a liquid that needs diluting for everyday use and a problem that can be caused if the dilution is not correct.

____

_______________ [2 marks]

D–C

b Sean says that solutions are made up of particles. How would he explain a concentrated solution?

_______________ [1 mark]

c Mary knows that to dilute an acid she must add the acid to the water and not the other way round. How would she dilute a solution of hydrochloric acid of 1 mol/dm^3 to make 100 cm^3 of a solution of 0.1 mol/dm^3?

____

_______________ [2 marks]

Titrations

Grades

G–E

1 a Look at the pH curve. It follows the reaction between an acid and an alkali. Write down what is happening at each stage.

A ______________________________

____

B ______________________________

____

C ______________________________

____

D ______________________________

____

[4 marks]

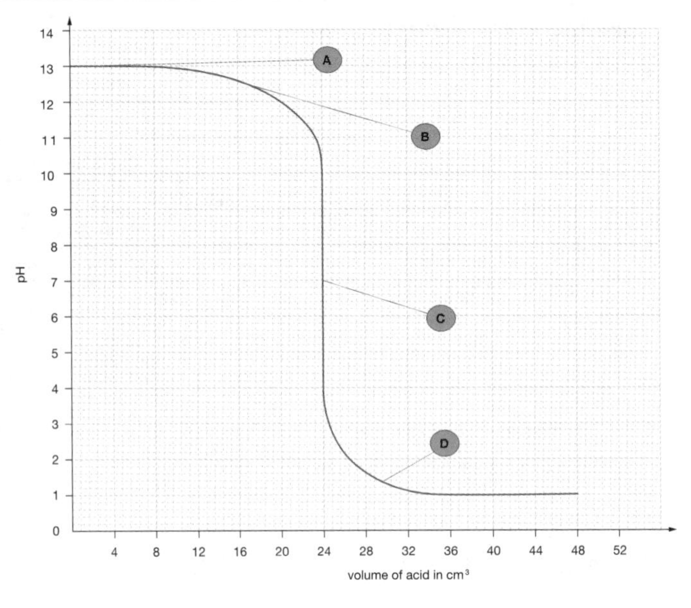

D–C

b When does the end point of this reaction happen? ______________________________ [1 mark]

c What is the pH when 28 cm^3 acid have been added? ______________________________ [1 mark]

d The pH changes during the reaction of an acid and an alkali. Explain why.

______________________________ [2 marks]

G–E

2 a Chen-chi carries out a titration. Look at the apparatus she uses.

i Label the pieces of apparatus.

ii Describe how she carries out an acid–alkali titration.

____

____

____

______________________________ [4 marks]

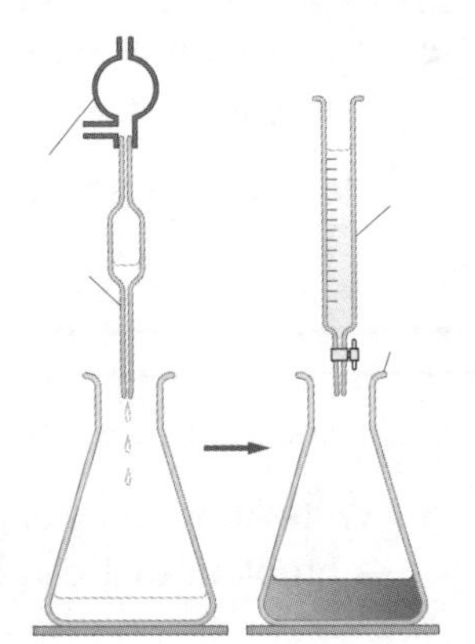

D–C

	volume of acid reacting with 25.0 cm^3 of alkali	
	rough	**first**
at start	1.2	3.2
at end	28.2	29.6
titre	27.0	

b What is the first titre that Chen-chi gets? ______________________________ [1 mark]

c Why does Chen-chi carry out several titrations?

______________________________ [1 mark]

Gas volumes

Grades

G–E

1 a Look at the three diagrams of apparatus used to collect volumes of gas.

Label the other two pieces used.

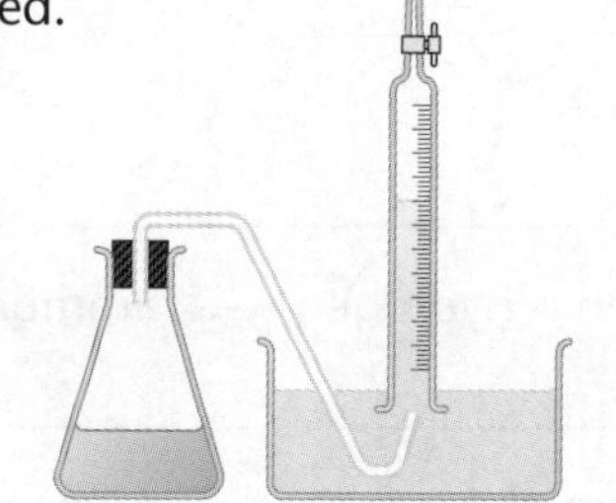

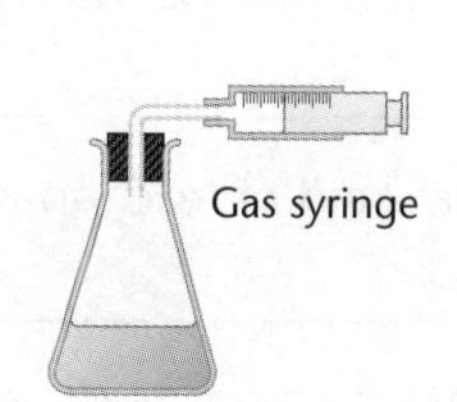

____ [2 marks]

b This piece of apparatus can be used to follow the amount gas being given off.

What is being measured?

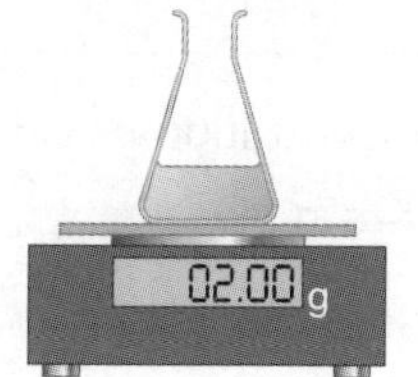

____ [1 mark]

c Asif measures the amount of gas given off when marble chips react with acid.

Describe how he does this, using a mass balance.

____

____

____ [3 marks]

D–C

d Haleema measures the amount of gas given off when magnesium reacts with acid.

She does this using a gas syringe. Describe how.

____

____

____ [3 marks]

2 Haleema drew a graph of her results, labelled reaction 1. She repeated the reaction but this time with only half the amount of magnesium. These results are reaction 2.

G–E

a What is the total volume of gas produced in reaction 1?

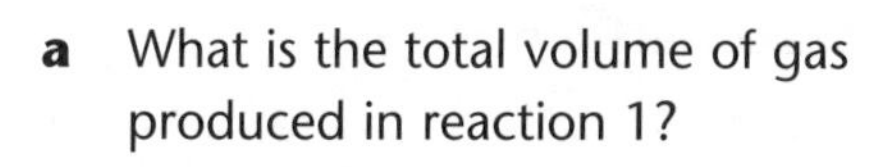

_______________________ [1 mark]

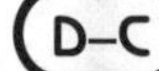

b At what time did reaction 1 stop? Why did it stop?

_______________________ [1 mark]

c In reaction 1, how much gas had she collected at 12 seconds?

_______________________ [1 mark]

d What is the total volume of gas produced in reaction 2?

volume in cm^3: 0, 2, 4, 6, 8, 10, 12, 14, 16, 18, 20, 22, 64, 26, 28

time in seconds: 0, 10, 20, 30, 40, 50, 60, 70, 80, 90, 100, 110, 120, 130

____ [1 mark]

e Explain why Haleema was predicting this volume of gas in reaction 2.

____ [1 mark]

Equilibria

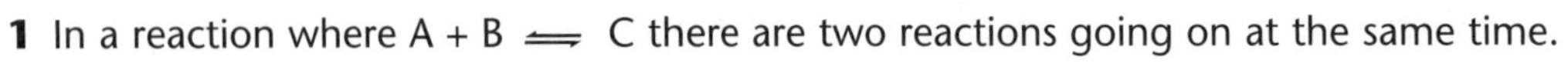

1 In a reaction where A + B ⇌ C there are two reactions going on at the same time.

A + B ⟶ C and C ⟶ A + B

G–E

a Which is the backward reaction?

______________________________ [1 mark]

b What kind of reaction is nitrogen + hydrogen ⇌ ammonia

______________________________ [1 mark]

D–C

c Some reactions reach equilibrium. If A + B ⇌ C reaches equilibrium, what does this tell us about the rate of the reactions?

______________________________ [1 mark]

d The concentration of C is greater than the concentration of A + B in the reaction A + B ⇌ C.

What does this tell us about where the equilibrium lies?

______________________________ [1 mark]

2 The percentage of ammonia made changes as the pressure and temperature of the reaction changes. Look at the graph.

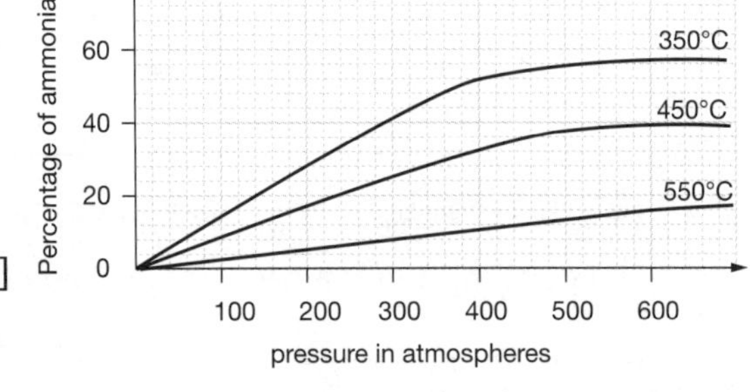

G–E

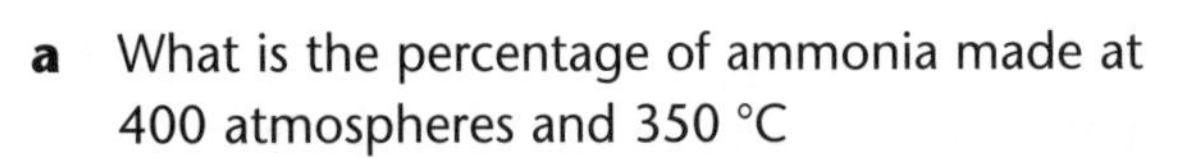

a What is the percentage of ammonia made at 400 atmospheres and 350 °C

______________________________ [1 mark]

D–C

b How does the percentage of ammonia change as the **pressure** increases?

______________________________ [1 mark]

c How does the percentage of ammonia change as the **temperature** increases?

______________________________ [1 mark]

G–E

3 a Sulfuric acid is made by a process. Put a (ring) around the correct process.

Haber **cracking** **electrolysis** **distillation** **Contact** [1 mark]

b What are the **three** raw materials used to make sulfuric acid?

______________________________ [3 marks]

c The production of sulfuric acid involves the reaction in this equation.

sulfur dioxide + oxygen ⇌ sulfur trioxide

i Which **two** substances combine to make sulfur trioxide?

______________________________ [1 mark]

ii What does the sign ⇌ mean?

______________________________ [1 mark]

D–C

iii What are the **three** conditions used in the process?

______________________________ [3 marks]

iv Where does the sulfur dioxide come from?

______________________________ [1 mark]

Strong and weak acids

G–E

1 a The acids in the table are either weak or strong. Complete the table.

hydrochloric acid	**nitric acid**	**ethanoic acid**	**sulphuric acid**

[2 marks]

b i Julie compares two acids, A and B. They both have the same concentration. B is a strong acid, A is a weak acid. How does she know B is a strong acid?

____ [1 mark]

D–C

ii Both acids ionise in water. Which ion is produced that makes the solution an acid?

____ [1 mark]

iii Both acids ionise to produce the same ion. Write down **how** B is a strong acid.

____ [2 marks]

iv When A ionises an equilibrium mixture is made. What **type** of reaction is this ionisation?

____ [1 mark]

G–E

2 a Ben and Gita react acids with magnesium and with calcium carbonate. Complete the first two rows of the table to show which **gases** were given off.

	hydrochloric acid	ethanoic acid
magnesium		
calcium carbonate		
speed of reaction		

[1 mark]

b They use the same **concentration** of acid. They notice that with both magnesium and calcium carbonate one acid reacts **faster**, one acts **slower**. Fill in the last row of the table. [1 mark]

D–C

c Explain why one acid reacts slower than the other. Use ideas about ions and collisions.

____ [2 marks]

G–E

3 Ben reacted hydrochloric acid with magnesium. Gita reacted ethanoic acid with magnesium. They each used the same amount of acid and the same amount of magnesium. They both measured the volume of gas they got every 10 seconds. Ben plotted his results as line C. Gita plotted her results as line D.

What conclusion do they make about the amount of gas produced. Put a (ring) around the correct answer.

Hydrochloric acid produces more gas
They produce the same amount of gas
Ethanoic acid produces more gas

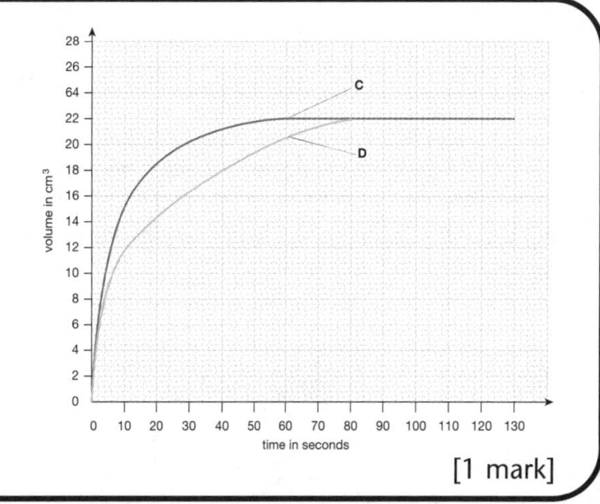

[1 mark]

D–C

4 a Ethanoic acid has a lower electrical conductivity than hydrochloric acid. Explain why.

____ [2 marks]

b If either acid is electrolysed, hydrogen is given off at the negative electrode. Explain why.

____ [2 marks]

Ionic equations

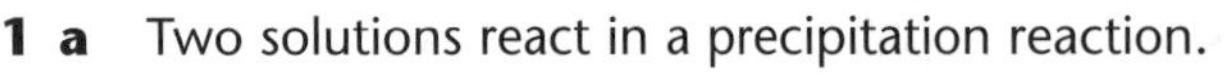

1 a Two solutions react in a precipitation reaction.

i What **type** of substance is made? Put a (ring) around the correct answer.

soluble **insoluble** **reactant** [1 mark]

ii What must the solutions contain for a precipitation reaction to happen? Put a (ring) around the correct answer.

molecules **hydrocarbons** **acids** **ions** [1 mark]

b Look at the diagram of a solid substance. What happens to the particles when the substance is heated or put into solution?

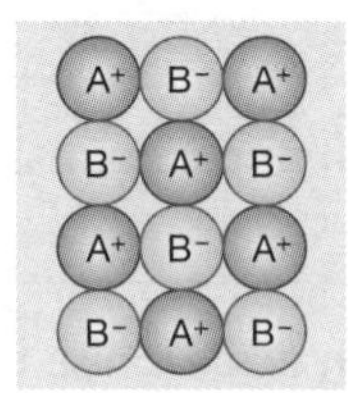

____ [1 mark]

G–E D–C

2 a Chris and Sam test solutions for halide ions. They put silver nitrate solution with each halide. Complete their table of what they would see.

solution	chloride	bromide	iodide
colour of precipitate			

[3 marks]

b They want to test for sulfate ions. Which test solution must they use?

____ [1 mark]

c They write an ionic equation for the reaction between potassium iodide and silver nitrate.

$$I^-_{(aq)} + AgNO_{3(aq)} \longrightarrow AgI_{(s)} + NO_3{}^-{}_{(aq)}$$

i Write down **one** reactant.

____ [1 mark]

ii Write down **one** product.

____ [1 mark]

iii In the equation there are the symbols (s) and (aq). What do these mean?

(s) ____________________ (aq) ____________________ [2 marks]

d Write a word equation for the reaction between silver nitrate and sodium bromide.

____ [2 marks]

G–E D–C

3 Chris and Sam make lead iodide. They use these pieces of apparatus.

Stage 1 ______________

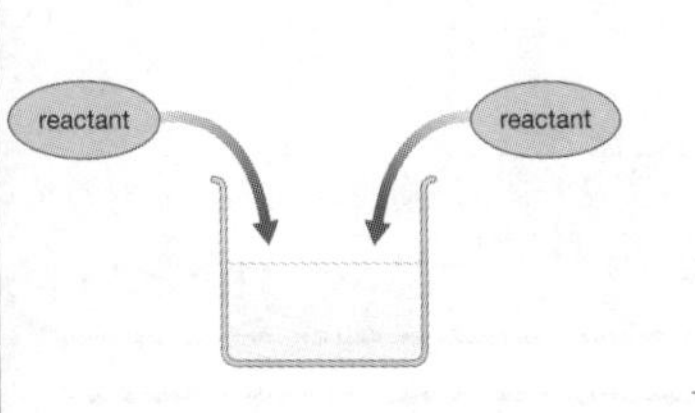

Stage 2 ______________

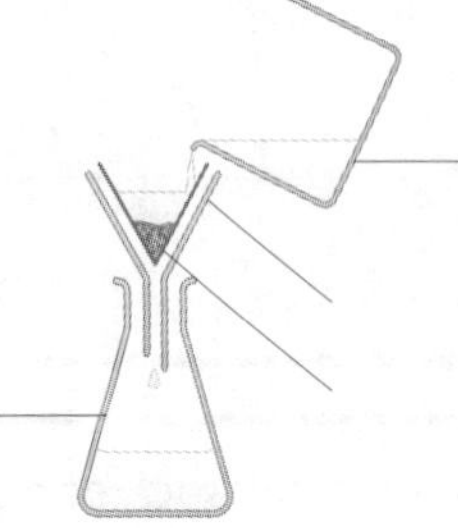

Stage 3 ______________

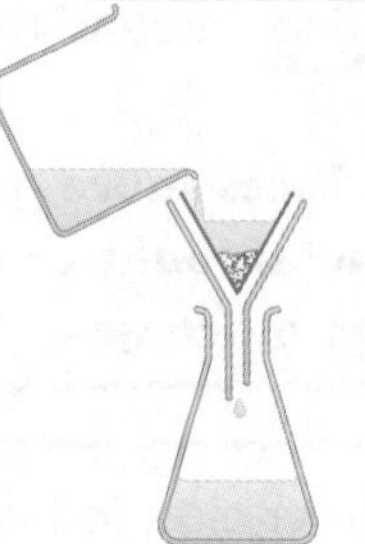

Stage 4 ______________

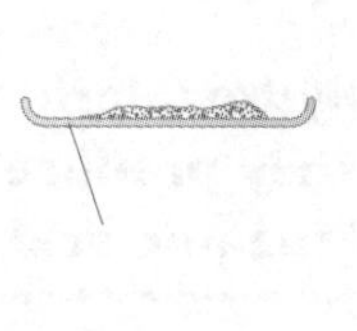

a Label the pieces of apparatus on the diagram. [5 marks]

b Complete the diagram by writing what Chris and Sam do at each stage. [4 marks]

D–C G–E

C5 Revision checklist

- I know that the molar mass of potassium hydroxide is 39 + 16 + 1 = 56
- I know that the empirical formula of glucose, $C_6H_{12}O_6$, is CH_2O
- I know that when lead bromide $PbBr_2$ is electrolysed, Pb and Br_2 are produced.
- I know that the amount made during electrolysis increases if time or current increases.
- I know that 1000 cm^3 equals 1 dm^3.
- I know that the more concentrated a solution, the more crowded the particles.
- I know how to label a burette, a pipette and a conical flask for a titration.
- I know that an acid added to an alkali produces a salt and water.
- I know that a reaction stops when one of the reactants is used up.
- I know how to do an experiment to measure the volume of gas given off.
- I know that in a reversible reaction there is a forward and a backward reaction.
- I know that the conditions needed for the Contact process are V_2O_5 catalyst, temperature of 450 °C and atmospheric pressure.
- I know that hydrochloric acid is a strong acid and ethanoic acid is a weak acid.
- I know that an acid ionises in water to produce H^+ ions.
- I know that silver nitrate can be used to test for chloride ions and that Cl^- ions make a white precipitate.
- I know that the word equation for the test for sulfate is:

  barium chloride + sodium sulfate → barium sulfate + sodium chloride

Energy transfers – fuel cells

Grades

1 a What is the test for hydrogen gas? (G–E)

____

______________________________ [2 marks]

b What is the test for oxygen gas?

____

______________________________ [2 marks]

c When oxygen and hydrogen react they do not produce a pollutant. (D–C)

What is made?

______________________________ [1 mark]

d When oxygen and hydrogen react heat is given out.

What type of reaction is this?

______________________________ [1 mark]

2 a In a fuel cell hydrogen and oxygen react together to produce a product. (G–E)

What energy is also produced?

______________________________ [1 mark]

b i Write a word equation for the reaction between hydrogen and oxygen. (D–C)

[ ] [ ] → [ ] [1 mark]

ii Describe how this reaction between hydrogen and oxygen is used to create a fuel cell.

______________________________ [1 mark]

3 a What is the fuel cell used for in a spacecraft? (G–E)

______________________________ [1 mark]

b There are advantages in using a fuel cell in a spacecraft. (D–C)

Write about **three** advantages.

____

____

______________________________ [3 marks]

c The car industry is developing fuel cells.

i Explain **two** advantages.

____

______________________________ [2 marks]

ii Write about **one** problem that will need to be overcome by the car when a fuel cell is used to power it.

______________________________ [1 mark]

Redox reactions

Grades

G–E

1 a If air and water attack iron, what is the common name for what is formed?

______________________________ [1 mark]

b What is the chemical name for what is formed?

______________________________ [1 mark]

D–C

c Write down the word equation for the reaction of iron, water and air.

[ ] [ ] [ ] → [ ] [2 marks]

G–E

2 a Write down the **six** ways to prevent the damage to iron in this reaction.

____

____

______________________________ [6 marks]

D–C

b Which **three** of these ways prevent air and water reaching the surface of the iron?

____

______________________________ [2 marks]

3 If metals are placed in solutions of metal salts, sometimes a reaction takes place.
Look at the table of results. The metals were put in a solution of tin sulfate at 20 °C.

metal	magnesium	tin	zinc	iron
temperature after 3 min in °C	32	20	28	23

G–E

a What conclusion can you make about the order of reactivity of the four metals?

____

______________________________ [3 marks]

b The same metals were put into solutions of metal salts. Look at the table of results.

	metal being added			
solution used	**magnesium**	**zinc**	**iron**	**tin**
magnesium sulfate	✗	✗	✗	✗
zinc sulfate	✓	✗	✗	✗
iron sulfate	✓	✓	✗	✗
tin sulfate	✓	✓	✓	✗

i With which metal salt solution or solutions did iron react?

______________________________ [1 mark]

ii Zinc metal did not react with the solution of magnesium salt. Give a reason why.

______________________________ [1 mark]

D–C

iii Write the word equation for a displacement reaction between zinc and a metal salt.

______________________________ [2 marks]

D–C

4 Why are redox reactions given the name 'redox'?

______________________________ [1 mark]

Alcohols

Grades

1 a Ethanol can be used as a fuel. What are the **two other** main uses of ethanol? G–E

1 ______

2 ______ [2 marks]

b Ethanol is made by fermentation. Explain why the fuel, ethanol, is a renewable fuel.

______ [1 mark]

c What are the **four** conditions needed for fermentation of glucose to take place?

1 ______

2 ______

3 ______

4 ______ [4 marks]

d Write down the word equation for the fermentation of glucose. D–C

[ ] → [ ] [ ] [2 marks]

e Ethanol often needs to be removed from the excess water. Describe how this is done.

______ [1 mark]

f i The molecular formula of ethanol has two carbon atoms and one oxygen atom in it. It also has hydrogen atoms. Write down the molecular formula for ethanol.

______ [1 mark]

ii Draw the displayed formula for ethanol.

[2 marks]

2 a Ethanol can also be made by the action of ethene and water. G–E

What is this **type** of reaction? ______ [1 mark]

b i Which catalyst is used in this reaction? ______ [1 mark]

ii Which conditions are used in this reaction? D–C

______ [1 mark]

c Write the word equation for this reaction.

______ [1 mark]

3 Ethanol can be heated with a different catalyst to produce ethene.

a What **type** of reaction is this? G–E

______ [1 mark]

heat

heat

b On the diagram label the catalyst used. [1 mark]

c Write the word equation for this reaction. D–C

______ [1 mark]

Chemistry of sodium chloride (NaCl)

Grades

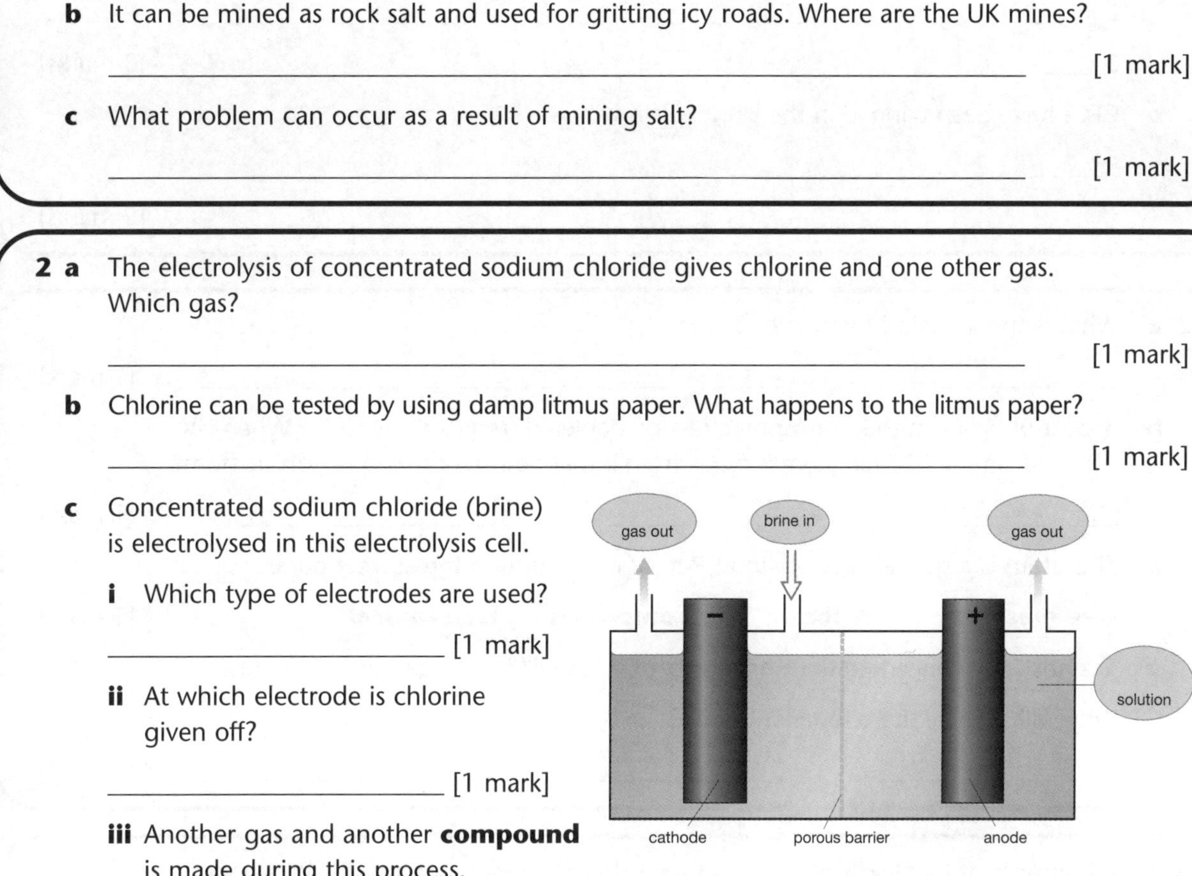

G–E

1 a Why is sodium chloride important?

____ [1 mark]

b It can be mined as rock salt and used for gritting icy roads. Where are the UK mines?

____ [1 mark]

D–C

c What problem can occur as a result of mining salt?

____ [1 mark]

G–E

2 a The electrolysis of concentrated sodium chloride gives chlorine and one other gas. Which gas?

____ [1 mark]

b Chlorine can be tested by using damp litmus paper. What happens to the litmus paper?

____ [1 mark]

D–C

c Concentrated sodium chloride (brine) is electrolysed in this electrolysis cell.

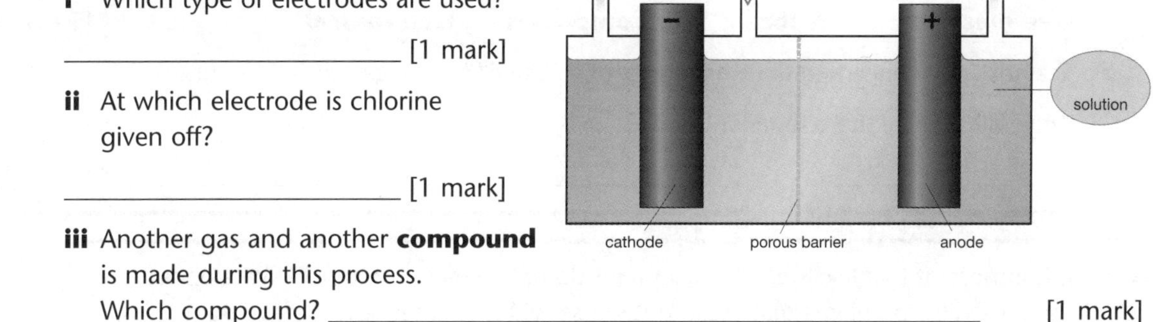

i Which type of electrodes are used?

____________________ [1 mark]

ii At which electrode is chlorine given off?

____________________ [1 mark]

iii Another gas and another **compound** is made during this process.
Which compound? ________________________________ [1 mark]

G–E

3 When molten (melted) sodium chloride is electrolysed there are two products at the electrodes.

a At which electrode is sodium metal deposited?

____ [1 mark]

b Which gas is given off at the other electrode?

____ [1 mark]

G–E

4 a For which **two** chemicals is sodium chloride an important source?

____________________ and ____________________ [2 marks]

b i Which **one** of these chemicals is used to make soap?

____ [1 mark]

ii The other chemical is a gas. It is used to sterilise water. Write **two other** uses for it.

____________________ and ____________________ [2 marks]

D–C

iii If the two chemicals are put together they make a substance with a household use.

Which use?

____ [1 mark]

Depletion of the ozone layer

Grades

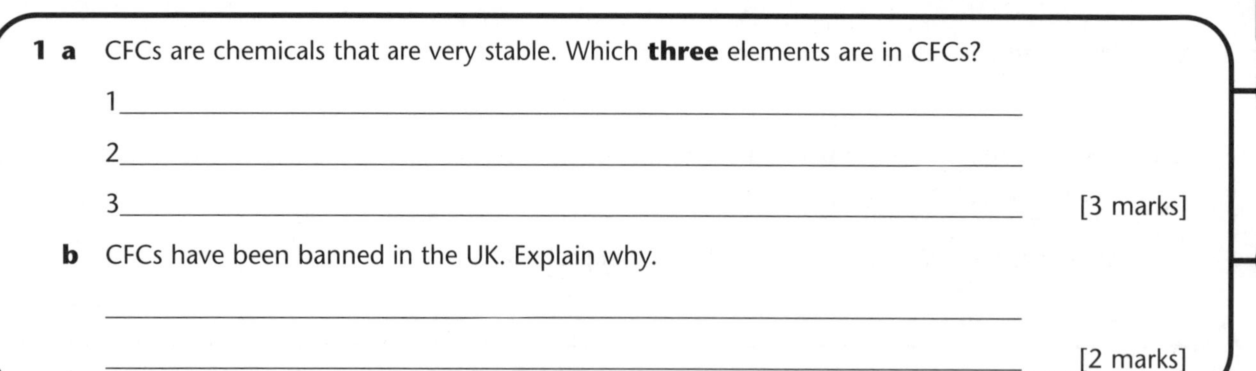

1 a CFCs are chemicals that are very stable. Which **three** elements are in CFCs? (G–E)

1 ______________________________

2 ______________________________

3 ______________________________ [3 marks]

b CFCs have been banned in the UK. Explain why. (D–C)

____

______________________________ [2 marks]

2 a What is the chemical formula of ozone? (G–E)

______________________________ [1 mark]

b A layer of ozone in the stratosphere can be depleted (reduced) by CFCs. When UV light acts on the CFC, an atom is made from it that destroys the ozone. Which atom? (D–C)

______________________________ [1 mark]

c This atom is a special type of atom. Put a (ring) around the correct phrase.

free electron **free ion** **free compound** **free radical** [1 mark]

d Scientists are concerned that the effects of CFCs will be noticed for a long time.

Why will they be there for a long time?

______________________________ [1 mark]

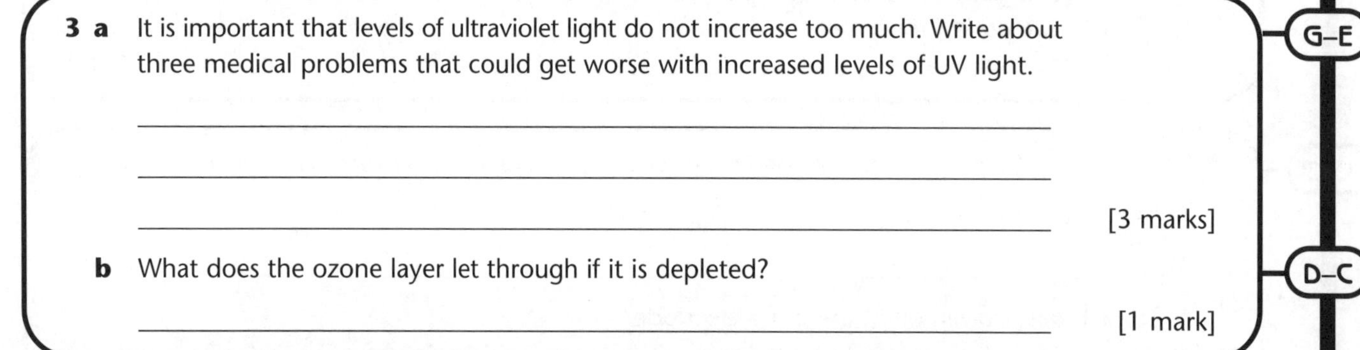

3 a It is important that levels of ultraviolet light do not increase too much. Write about three medical problems that could get worse with increased levels of UV light. (G–E)

____

____

______________________________ [3 marks]

b What does the ozone layer let through if it is depleted? (D–C)

______________________________ [1 mark]

4 a Which kinds of compounds are now used as safer alternatives to CFCs? (D–C)

______________________________ [1 mark]

b Look at the diagram of the types of molecules that are sources of chlorine atoms in the stratosphere.

22% CCl_4/ $C_2H_3Cl_3$

18% natural

9% mixed CFC

51% synthetic CFC

What percentage of these gases are artificial?

______________________________ [1 mark]

Hardness of water

Grades

G–E

1 a How does hard water act with soap?

______________________________ [1 mark]

D–C

b Rainwater dissolves carbon dioxide. How does this change the rainwater?

______________________________ [1 mark]

c Rainwater with carbon dioxide reacts with rocks made of calcium carbonate to form soluble calcium hydrogencarbonate.

Write a word equation for this reaction.

[ ] [ ] [ ] → [ ] [2 marks]

G–E

2 a Which **two** ions cause hardness in water?

______________ and ______________ [2 marks]

b There are two ways that **all** types of hardness in water can be removed.

One way is using an ion exchange column. Write down the other way.

______________________________ [1 mark]

D–C

c Describe how an ion exchange resin can soften water.

______________________________ [2 marks]

G–E

3 a There are two types of hardness in water, permanent and temporary.

How can temporary hardness be removed?

______________________________ [1 mark]

D–C

b Which chemical compound causes temporary hardness?

______________________________ [1 mark]

G–E

4 a Look at the table.

sample of water	A	B	C	D
height of soap lather before boiling in mm	40	2	3	3
height of soap lather after boiling in mm	40	22	3	38

D–C

i Which **one** of the samples of water may have contained water that was permanently hard?

______________________________ [1 mark]

ii Explain how you know this from the data in the table.

______________________________ [2 marks]

b Jo and Sam got these results when they carried out an investigation. They needed to make sure their experiments were fair tests. Write down **two** ways they did this.

1______________________________

2______________________________ [2 marks]

Natural fats and oils

Grades

1 a i Write down **one** example of an animal fat. (G–E)

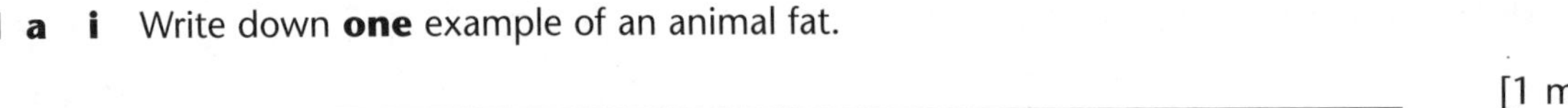

[1 mark]

b Write down **one** example of a vegetable oil.

[1 mark]

c Diesel is usually made from crude oil. Describe an alternative way diesel can be made.

[1 mark]

2 a Oils and fats belong to one group of chemical compounds. What is this group? (D–C)

[1 mark]

b Look at the two displayed formulae, M and N.

```
  H   H   H   H   H   H   H           H   H   H   H       H   H
  |   |   |   |   |   |   |           |   |   |   |       |   |
 -C - C - C - C - C - C - C-         -C - C - C - C = C - C - C-
  |   |   |   |   |   |   |           |   |   |       |   |   |
  H   H   H   H   H   H   H           H   H   H       H   H   H

              M                                   N
```

i M is a saturated compound. Explain how you know.

[1 mark]

ii Circle the part of the compound of N that shows it is an unsaturated compound.

[1 mark]

c Bromine water can be used to show the difference between M and N.

i Describe what you would do to test the difference.

[1 mark]

ii Describe what you would **see**.

[2 marks]

3 a What is an emulsion? (G–E)

[1 mark]

b What **type** of emulsion is butter?

[1 mark]

4 a What is added to natural fats and oils to make soap? (G–E)

[1 mark]

b When soap is made, the chemical splits the oil making glycerol as well. (D–C)

What is this process called?

[1 mark]

Analgesics

Grades

G–E

1 a What is the job of a person who is trained to sell analgesics?

____ [1 mark]

b Aspirin is an analgesic, write down the name of one other analgesic.

____ [1 mark]

D–C

2 Look at the displayed formula of one analgesic, X. The molecular formula is $C_8H_9O_2N$.

Look at the displayed formula of aspirin. What is its molecular formula?

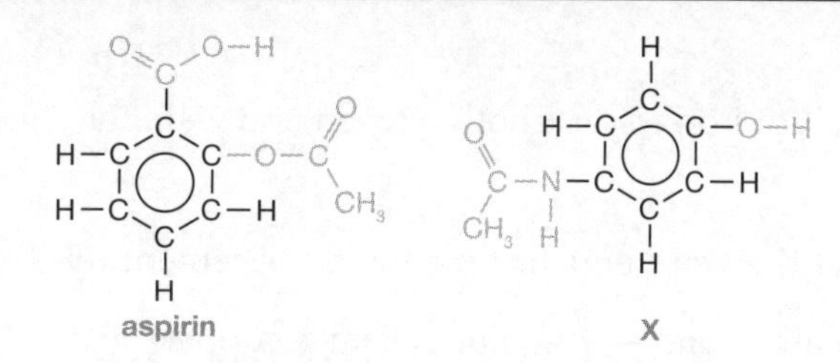

____ [2 marks]

3 a Write down the **three** reasons for taking aspirin to relieve symptoms of illness.

1____

2____

3____ [3 marks]

D–C

b It is important to take the right dose of aspirin. Write down **one** danger of taking an overdose of aspirin.

____ [1 mark]

c There is an advantage in taking soluble aspirin. What is it?

____ [1 mark]

4 a Aspirin is now made synthetically. In what was aspirin first discovered?

____ [1 mark]

D–C

b i Why is an analgesic, like aspirin, described as a drug?

____

____ [2 marks]

ii Why must the chemicals used to make a drug be very pure?

____ [1 mark]

C6 Revision checklist

- I know that when a lighted splint is put into a test tube of gas and a squeaky pop is heard, the gas is hydrogen. ☐
- I know that a fuel cell is supplied with fuel and oxygen and the energy from the reaction between them is used to create a potential difference. ☐
- I know that for iron to rust, both oxygen and water are needed. ☐
- I know that the word equation for the displacement reaction between copper sulfate and zinc is: copper sulfate + zinc $\longrightarrow$ zinc sulfate + copper ☐
- I know that the conditions for fermentation are 25–50 °C, water, enzymes in yeast and no oxygen. ☐
- I know that the word equation for the hydration of ethene is: ethene + water $\longrightarrow$ ethanol ☐
- I know that the chemical test for chlorine is that it bleaches moist litmus paper. ☐
- I know that in the electrolysis of brine (concentrated sodium chloride solution), hydrogen is made at the cathode, chlorine is made at the anode and sodium hydroxide is also made. ☐
- I know that depletion of the ozone layer allows more ultraviolet light to reach the surface of the Earth which can lead to increased risks of sunburn, cataracts and skin cancer. ☐
- I know that the formation of chlorine atoms (free radicals) in the stratosphere leads to the depletion of the ozone layer. ☐
- I know that hardness in water is caused by dissolved calcium and magnesium ions in water. ☐
- I know that boiling removes temporary hardness but not permanent hardness in water. Calcium hydrogencarbonate decomposes to give insoluble calcium carbonate. ☐
- I know that an emulsion is one liquid finely dispersed in another liquid. ☐
- I know that an unsaturated fat or oil has at least one carbon–carbon double bond. ☐
- I know that the beneficial effects of aspirin are that it reduces pain, lowers body temperature and thins the blood to reduce the risk of blood clots. ☐
- know that I can work out the molecular formula of aspirin from its displayed formula. ☐

Glossary

A

acidic A chemical that turns litmus paper red with a pH below 7.
alcohol A liquid produced when yeast respires sugar in the absence of oxygen.
alkali A substance which makes a solution that turns red litmus paper blue.
alkali metal A metal which burns to form a strongly alkaline oxide, e.g. potassium, sodium.
alkane Chemicals containing only hydrogen and carbon with the general formula C_nH_{2n+2}, e.g. methane.
alkene Chemicals containing only hydrogen and carbon with the general formula C_nH_{2n}, e.g. ethene.
allotrope Different forms of the same element made when the atoms of the element join together in different patterns, e.g. diamond and graphite are allotropes of carbon.
alloy A mixture of two or more metals.
ammonia An alkaline gas with the formula NH_3; it dissolves readily in water to make ammonium hydroxide solution.
analgesics A painkiller.
anion A negatively charged ion; it will move towards the anode in an electrolytic cell.
anode The positive electrode in a circuit or battery.
antioxidant Chemicals which delay the oxidation of other chemicals. They are important in paints, plastics and rubbers where they slow down degradation of the material. Vitamin C is an antioxidant in the body.
ascorbic acid The chemical name for vitamin C.
aspirin A painkilling drug originally made from the bark of willow trees.
atom The smallest part of an element, atoms consist of negatively charged electrons flying around a positively charged nucleus.
atomic number The number of protons in the nucleus of an atom.

B

base An alkali.
batch process A process that has a clear start and finish; often used to make medicines, at the end of the process a batch of product has been made and the reaction stops.
bauxite A mineral containing aluminium.
binding medium The substance, usually a thin glue, used to support pigments in paints.
biodegradable A substance which can be broken down by biological action in the environment.
biofuel A fuel that is produced from a living system, e.g. wood or ethanol produced from maize starch.
buckminster fullerene A very stable ball of 60 carbon atoms joined by covalent bonds; the whole structure looks like a geodesic dome.
bulk properties Properties that are independent of the amount of substance being measured, e.g. density or refractive index.
burette A glass device for measuring volumes of liquids very accurately; burettes are used in titrations.

C

carbohydrate Chemical found in all living things that contains the elements carbon, hydrogen and oxygen. Sugars are carbohydrates which dissolve in water and taste sweet. Starches are carbohydrates which cannot dissolve in water and do not taste sweet.
carbon A very important element, carbon is present in all living things and forms a huge range of compounds with other elements.
carbon dioxide A gas containing only carbon and oxygen; its chemical formula is CO_2.
carbon monoxide A poisonous gas containing only carbon and oxygen; its chemical formula is CO.
carbonate Compounds containing the carbonate group of atoms; the carbonate group formula is CO_3.
catalyst A chemical that speeds up a reaction but is not changed or used up by the reaction.
catalytic converter Boxes fitted to vehicle exhausts which reduce the level of nitrogen oxides and unburnt hydrocarbons in the exhaust fumes.
cathode The negative electrode in a circuit or a battery.
cation A positively charged ion; it moves towards the cathode in an electrolytic cell.
CFCs Chlorofluorocarbons are chemicals containing carbon, hydrogen, chlorine and fluorine; they were used in the past in refrigerators and as propellants in aerosols but have been phased out because they seem to damage the ozone layer.
chemical change A change that occurs when a number of substances react together to produce new substances.
chemical property The characteristic reactions of a substance.
chlorination Adding chlorine to a molecule or substance.
chromatography The science of producing chromatograms, chromatography can use paper or jelly-like films for the soluble substances to move along.
collision frequency The number of collisions in a particular area in a particular time.
colloid A mixture in which small particles of one substance are suspended in another.
combustion The reaction between a fuel and oxygen to form carbon dioxide and water; energy is released as light and heat.
compound A group of atoms bound together, in fixed proportions, by chemical bonds; compounds have different chemical and physical properties to the elements that they contain.
compression To push something together, to squeeze it and make it smaller.
concentration The amount of solute in a solution in g/dm^3.
conductor A substance that will let heat or electricity pass through it, e.g. copper.
Contact Process The industrial process for the manufacture of sulfuric acid using a catalyst (usually vanadium (V) oxide), temperatures of 450 °C and pressures of 200 kPa.
continental plate A large plate of solid rock in the Earth's crust containing a continental landmass.
continuous process A process which can continue indefinitely if new materials are added and wastes removed.

convection current Movement upwards of heated gases or liquids to float on top of the cooler, denser layers.
corrode Reaction of metals with the air to form powder or crystals, weakening the metal; the term rust is used when iron corrodes.
covalent bond A link between two atoms where electrons move around both atoms in the pair; covalent bonds tend to be strong bonds and form between non-metals.
cracking The breaking of large organic molecules into smaller ones using heat, pressure and sometimes catalysts.
critical temperature The temperature at which a key event takes place, perhaps a reaction starts or an animal dies.
crop yield The mass of useful material produced by a crop.
cryolite A compound of fluorine, aluminium and sodium (Na_3AlF_6) used to extract aluminium from bauxite by electrolysis.
crystals A solid substance with a regular shape made up of flat planes.

D
decompose To break apart.
delocalised electron An electron in a molecule that is not linked directly to an individual atom or covalent bond.
density The mass of an object divided by its volume.
diffusion Diffusion is the spreading of gases or liquids caused by the random movement of their molecules.
discharge To lose charge.
displacement reaction A reaction where one chemical, usually a metal, is forced out of a compound by another chemical, also usually a metal.
displayed formula A formula that shows all the bonds in the molecule as individual lines.
dissolve When a solid mixes in with a liquid so that it cannot be seen.
distillation Used to boil off a liquid from a mixture and then cool the vapours to produce a purer liquid.
dot and cross model A way to show how electrons are shared in covalent bonds.
ductile Can be drawn into a thin wire; metals are ductile.

E
efficient An efficient device transfers most of the input energy into the desired output energy.
electrode Bars of metal or carbon that carry electric current into a liquid.
electrolysis Using an electric current to split a compound – either in solution or in its molten state.
electrolyte The liquid carrying the electric current in an electric cell.
electromagnet A magnet produced by an electric current passing through a coil of wire.
electron A small negatively charged particle that orbits around the nucleus of an atom.
electron pattern The way electrons are arranged in a substance.
electronic structure The way electrons are arranged in the shells around an atom.
electrostatic To do with electric charges that are not moving; electrostatic charges behave differently to current electricity.
element A substance that cannot be split into anything simpler by chemical means, all the atoms of an element have the same atomic number although some may have different atomic masses.
emulsions Formed when tiny droplets of oil are dispersed through water (oil-in-water emulsion, e.g. milk) or water is dispersed through oil (water-in-oil emulsion, e.g. butter).
emulsifier A chemical which can help to break fats up into small globules so that they do not settle out of suspension.
endothermic A reaction that takes in energy when it happens.
equilibrium A balancing position.
eutrophication Waters with very high levels of minerals, often created by fertiliser pollution, producing a very heavy growth of algae.
exothermic A reaction which gives out energy when it happens.

F
fats A type of food that is very rich in energy, found in chocolate, butter and margarine and the fat on bacon and other meats.
fermentation Breakdown of food by microorganisms that does not require oxygen.
fertiliser A substance added to the ground by gardeners and farmers to help plants to grow.
filtration The process of separating large particles from small ones using a filter.
finite resource Resources that will run out because they are not being produced at the same rate as they are being used up.
formula A shorthand way to show the type and amount of elements present in a compound.
formula, empirical A formula that indicates the relative proportions of the elements in a molecule rather than the actual number of atoms of the elements.
fossil fuel A fuel formed by the decay of dead living things over millions of years, e.g. coal, oil and natural gas.
free radical A covalent bond, made of two electrons, when broken by UV, splits into equal halves to make two free radicals. Free radicals are highly reactive.
fuel Something that gives out energy, usually as light and heat, when it burns.
fuel cells Cells that use chemical reactions to generate electricity.
fullerene A cage-like arrangement of carbon atoms.

G
gas syringe A glass syringe used to measure volumes of gases very accurately.
giant ionic lattice A large collection of ions held together by strong electrostatic charges.
gradient A slope or difference in measurements between two areas, e.g. there is a concentration gradient between the water molecules inside and those outside a cell.
graphite A type of carbon often used in pencils as the 'lead'.
greenhouse gas Gases such as carbon dioxide and water vapour that increase the greenhouse effect.

H
Haber process The industrial process developed by Fritz Haber to make ammonia from nitrogen and hydrogen.
halogen A group of reactive non-metals with only one electron missing from their outer electron shell, e.g. chlorine and iodine.
hard water Water containing dissolved magnesium and calcium salts, mainly bicarbonates, which make it difficult for soap to form a lather.

hydrocarbon Hydrocarbon molecules are molecules that contain only carbon and hydrogen atoms. Many fuels are hydrocarbons, e.g. natural gas (methane) and petrol (a complex mixture).
hydrogen A colourless, odourless gas that burns easily in oxygen to form water; hydrogen is the lightest element.
hydrogen bond A force of attraction between the hydrogen atom in a molecule and a strongly electronegative atom such as nitrogen or oxygen.
hydrophilic A molecule or part of a molecule that dissolves easily in water; 'water loving'.
hydrophobic A molecule or part of a molecule that does not dissolve easily in water; 'water hating'.
hydroxide Chemicals containing an 'OH' group; hydroxides are often alkaline.

I

igneous Rocks formed from solidified molten magma.
indicator A chemical that changes colour in acid and alkaline solutions; indicators are used to find the pH of a solution.
insoluble A substance that will not dissolve; something that is insoluble in water may be soluble in other liquids.
intermolecular force A force between two molecules.
ion Charged particle made when an atom, or group of atoms, gains or loses electrons.
ionic exchange The exchange of ions to remove hardness in water using resins. Water flows over solid resin which traps calcium and magnesium ions on to it, taking these ions out of the water. They are exchanged for sodium ions.
ionic equation An equation showing the movement and behaviour of ions in a reaction.
isotope One of two or more atoms having the same atomic number but different mass numbers.

K

kinetic energy Energy due to movement.

L

lattice A regular arrangement of items, often applied to a collection of ions in a crystal.
lava Molten rock thrown up by a volcano.
limescale Deposit of calcium carbonate caused by boiling temporary hard water.
lithosphere The outer part of the earth, consisting of the crust and upper mantle, approximately 100 km thick.
lustrous Having a sheen or glow; highly polished metals such as gold are often described as lustrous.

M

magma Molten rock inside the Earth.
magnesium A lightweight, silvery white metal which burns with a very bright white flame.
malleable Can be beaten into flat sheets; metals are malleable.
mass Mass describes the amount of something - it is measured in kilograms.
mass number The mass of an atom compared with hydrogen.
melting point The temperature at which a solid changes to a liquid.
metal halide A compound containing only a metal and a halogen atom, e.g. sodium chloride.
metallic bond The bond typical of metals in which electrons are shared between many atoms in a stable crystalline structure.
metamorphic Rock formed when heat and pressure changes the characteristics of an existing rock.
methane A colourless, odourless gas that burns easily to give water and carbon dioxide.
mineral Natural solid materials with a fixed chemical composition and structure; rocks are made of collections of minerals; mineral nutrients in our diet are simple chemicals needed for health, e.g. calcium and iron.
molecular formula A formula that shows the number and kinds of atoms in a molecule.
molecule A group of atoms joined together by chemical links.
moles A mole of any substance contains 6×1023 particles of that substance, it weighs the atomic weight of the substance expressed in grams.
molten Something that has been heated to change it from a solid to a liquid.

N

nano properties The properties of materials at the nanoscale, often different to the same material's properties at the visible scale.
nanoparticle A particle that has at least one dimension that is smaller than 100 nanometres; a nanometre is 10^{-9} m.
nanoscale Objects and events occurring at distances of fewer than 100 nanometres.
nanotube A molecule consisting of carbon atoms joined in a cylinder one to two nanometres in diameter and about a millimetre in length.
naphtha A group of generally liquid chemicals derived from crude oil by distillation.
negative ion An ion with a negative charge.
neutral A neutral solution has a pH of 7 and is neither acid nor alkaline.
neutralise To react an acid with an alkali to produce a neutral solution.
neutron A particle found in the nucleus of an atom, it has no electrical charge and a mass of 1 atomic mass unit.
nitinol An alloy of nickel and titanium that has the ability to return to a predetermined shape when heated.
nitrogen A non-reactive gas that makes up most of the atmosphere.
nitrogenous Chemicals containing nitrogen.
non-biodegradable Objects that cannot be broken down by living organisms, e.g. many plastics, so they last for an extremely long time in the environment.
nucleus The control centre of the cell, the nucleus is surrounded by a membrane that separates it from the rest of the cell; the central part of an atom containing the protons and neutrons.

O

oils Fatty chemicals.
opaque Opaque objects will not let light through so they make a shadow, e.g. black paper.
optimum temperature The temperature range that produces the best reaction rate.
oxidation A reaction which adds oxygen to a compound or element, e.g. combustion and respiration.
oxidising Agent chemicals which supply oxygen or receive electrons in a chemical reaction, e.g. air and bleach.
oxygen A colourless gas with no smell that makes up about 20% of the air.
ozone layer A layer of the upper atmosphere that is particularly rich in the gas ozone.

P

particles A very small part of something.
patent A law that gives the creator of an invention the sole right to make, use or sell that invention for a given period of time.
period A horizontal row of the periodic table.
periodic table A way of grouping elements according to their similarities, first devised by Dimitri Mendeleev.
permanent hardness Hardness in water due to calcium sulfate; it cannot be removed by boiling.
pH meter An electronic device for measuring the pH of a solution.
pH scale The range of levels of acidity or alkalinity; a pH of 7 is neutral, a pH below 7 is acid and the lower it goes the more acidic it becomes. A pH above 7 is alkaline.
phosphorescent Phosphorescent materials glow gently even after the original light source has been removed.
pigment Chemicals which absorb certain wavelengths of light and so look coloured.
pollutant A chemical that causes pollution.
polymer A molecule made of many repeating subunits, for example polythene or starch.
polymerisation The process of forming large polymers from smaller monomer molecules.
positive ion An ion with a positive charge.
precipitate A insoluble solid formed suddenly when two solutions react together.
product Something made by a chemical reaction.
proton A particle found in the nucleus of an atom with a charge of plus one and a mass of one atomic mass unit.

R

reactant A chemical taking part in a chemical reaction.
reaction time The time taken for a reaction to finish.
reactivity A measure of how easily a chemical will react, usually applied to the reaction between metals and water.
recommended daily allowance The amount dieticians recommend for a healthy diet.
redox reactions Reactions that involve oxidation and reduction.
reducing agents Chemicals that take in oxygen or give electrons away in a chemical reaction, e.g. methane in a gas burner.
reduction The loss of oxygen or the gaining of hydrogen in a reaction.
relative atomic mass The mass of an atom or particle in comparison to the mass of hydrogen, which is taken as 1.
relative formula mass The mass of a molecule in comparison to the mass of hydrogen, which is taken as 1.
renewable Sources of energy that will not run out such as wind power, wave power and solar power.
reversible reaction A reaction whose direction can be changed by a change in conditions.

S

salt A compound made when an acid reacts with an alkali.
saponification Heating vegetable oils with sodium hydroxide solution in large vats in the manufacture of soap.
saturated A solution that cannot dissolve any more solute.
sedimentary Rock formed when sediments from other rocks are laid down and compacted together.
sedimentation Particles settling out of suspension in water.
shell A grouping of electrons around an atom.
soluble A substance that can dissolve in a liquid, e.g. sugar is soluble in water.
solute Something that dissolves in a liquid to form a solution.
solution Something formed when a solute dissolves in a liquid.
solvent The liquid that dissolves a solute to make a solution.
stable electronic structure A configuration of electrons in the shells around an atom that produces a stable structure.
stable octet The most stable structure for the second shell around an atom.
strength of acid The degree to which an acid ionises.
surface area The area of a surface, which has a significant effect on the rate of many chemical reactions.
synthetic Made by humans, e.g. plastics are synthetic compounds which do not occur naturally.

T

tectonic plate Sections of the Earth's crust that float on top of the mantle. Plates are hundreds of miles across and move relative to each other by a few inches a year.
temporary hardness Hardness of water caused by calcium hydrogencarbonate. It can be removed by boiling the water.
tensile strength The maximum force a material can withstand before it snaps.
thermal To do with heat.
thermal decomposition Breaking down a chemical using heat.
thermochromic A pigment that changes colour when it gets hotter or colder.
titration Adding carefully measured amounts of a solution of known concentration to an unknown one to reach an end point which allows the concentration of materials in the unknown solution to be calculated.
transition element A metal belonging to the transition group in the periodic table.

U

Universal indicator solution An indicator that changes colour in solutions of different pH.
unsaturated A solution that can dissolve more solute. An unsaturated hydrocarbon can react with more hydrogen because it contains a number of double-carbon bonds.

Y

yeast A unicellular fungus used extensively in the brewing and baking industries.
yield The ratio of product to starting materials; a high yield means that most of the starting material is converted to useful products.

Answers

Here are the answers to the topic questions from the revision guide pages, and the answers to the exam-practice questions in the workbook.

This section is perforated, so that you can remove the answers to help test yourself or a friend.

C1 Carbon chemistry

Page 5

1 Cannot change back.
2 They change shape.
3 Decomposes means that it breaks down. The three products are sodium carbonate, carbon dioxide and water.
4 It turns from colourless to cloudy (milky).

Page 6

1 An antioxidant.
2 Packaging that uses sensors to monitor the quality of the food.
3 Detergent.
4 The 'fat-loving' tail and 'water-loving' head act together to form emulsions.

Page 7

1 Esters.
2 One person may object to cosmetics being tested on animals, as the animals may be harmed and they have no control over what happens to them. The other may say that they feel safer if the cosmetics have been tested on animals.
3 Acid and alcohol.
4 Soluble.

Page 8

1 A fuel formed from the compression of dead animals and plants over millions of years.
2 At the top.
3 The breaking down of large hydrocarbon molecules to smaller, more useful ones such as petrol.
4 C_7H_{16}.

Page 9

1 Polystyrene.
2 High pressure and a catalyst.
3 Ethane.
4 Alkanes do not have a double C=C bond, alkenes do.

Page 10

1 Waterproof and rigid.
2 It makes people sweat as it is not breathable.
3 Is not decomposed by bacteria.
4 Toxic gases.

Page 11

1 Oxygen.
2 Blue.
3 Limewater.
4 Less soot is made, more heat is released and toxic carbon monoxide gas is not produced.

Page 12

1 Any two from: heat, light, sound, electricity.
2 A chemical reaction in which energy is transferred to the surroundings (energy is released).
3 Same mass of water, same mass of fuel.
4 Yellow flame.

C2 Rocks and metals

Page 14

1 To thin the paint.
2 A **colloid** is when small solid particles are dispersed through the whole of a liquid, but are not dissolved in it.
3 A pigment that changes colour when it is heated.
4 The use of synthetic dyes has increased.

Page 15

1 Any three from: granite, marble, limestone, aluminium, iron (steel), brick, cement, concrete, glass.
2 Limestone and clay.
3 Calcium carbonate.
4 Calcium oxide and carbon dioxide.

Page 16

1 Iron core, mantle and crust.
2 They are less dense.
3 Igneous.
4 If the magma cools slowly, large crystals are made. Rapid cooling produces smaller crystals.

Page 17

1 To save resources and money.
2 The cathode.
3 An alloy is a mixture of a metal element with another element.
4 Copper and zinc.

Page 18

1 Water and oxygen.
2 The oxide of aluminium becomes a protective layer.
3 Iron.
4 Aluminium will corrode less and produce a lighter car than steel.

Page 19

1 It increases the level of carbon dioxide and decreases the level of oxygen.
2 Photosynthesis.
3 Sulphur dioxide.
4 Changes carbon monoxide to carbon dioxide, and oxides of nitrogen to nitrogen.

Page 20

1 Altering any three from: concentration of the reactants, temperature of the reactants, pressure of reactants that are gases, surface area of the reactants.
2 For a reaction to take place particles must collide often enough, with sufficient energy. If the particles move faster they will collide more successfully. If they are more crowded they will collide more often. In both cases the reaction will be faster.
3 Collecting the hydrogen given off with a gas syringe.
4 At a higher temperature the particles have more energy, so they collide more successfully, so the reaction is quicker. However, if the same mass of magnesium is used it will produce the same volume of hydrogen each time.

Page 21

1 Any two from: sulphur, flour, custard powder, wood dust.
2 Powdered reactants.
3 Half the mass of zinc will produce only half the volume of gas if the acid remains in excess both times.
4 A substance that is able to speed up a reaction but that is not used up in the reaction.

C3 The periodic table

Page 23

1 Positive.
2 1.
3 11.
4 Copper and sulphur.

Page 24

1 An ion.
2 Electrons are gained.
3 A metal atom needs to lose electrons. The electrons transfer from the metal atom to a non-metal atom. A non-metal atom needs to gain electrons. The electrons transfer to the non-metal atom from the metal atom.
4 It is very high.

Page 25

1 Three.
2

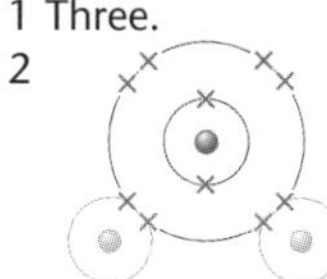

3 Fluorine and chlorine.
4 Third.

Page 26

1 Because they react with air and water.
2 Because it is less dense than water.
3 They all have one electron in their outer shell.
4 Potassium.

Page 27

1 Halogens.
2 Chlorine.
3 Potassium + bromine → potassium bromide.
4 Iodine is less reactive than bromine, so does not displace it.

Page 28

1 The anode.
2 The formula of the compound breaking up is H_2O.
3 Bauxite.
4 They are worn away by oxidation.

Page 29

1 Cu and Ni.
2 Orange/brown.
3 A reaction between solutions that makes an insoluble solid.
4 In sodium hydroxide solution, Fe^{2+} ions form a grey/green solid and Fe^{3+} ions form an orange gelatinous solid.

Page 30

1 Any three from: lustrous, good conductors of heat and electricity, hard, high melting point, high boiling point, high density.
2 They have strong metallic bonds between the atoms that are very hard to break and a lot of energy is needed to separate them.
3 They become superconductors.
4 It levitates.

C4 Chemical economics

Page 32

1 Any two from: making fertilisers, cleaning materials, car battery acids.
2 Zinc oxide, zinc hydroxide or zinc carbonate.
3 pH 1-6.
4 Magnesium sulfate.

Page 33

1 $65 + 12 + (3 \times 16) = 65 + 12 + 48 = 125$
2 $40 + 2(14 + (3 \times 16)) = 40 + 2(14 + 48) = 40 + 2(62) = 40 + 124 = 164$
3 Any two from: filtration losses, evaporation losses, losses when transferring liquids, more than one reaction taking place.
4 75%.

Page 34

1 Potassium and phosphorus.
2 149.
3 Any two from: ammonium nitrate, ammonium phosphate, ammonium sulphate, urea.
4 Potassium hydroxide and phosphoric acid.

Page 35
1 Nitrogen and hydrogen.
2 About 450 °C.
3 Any three from: building the plant, people's wages, raw materials, energy, catalyst.
4. The yield would be too low.

Page 36
1 To allow clothes to be washed at low temperatures.
2 An organic acid and an alkali.
3 A solvent.
4 Fabrics may be damaged by washing in water; grease stains do not dissolve in water but do in dry-cleaning solvent.

Page 37
1 Where the process does not stop and reactants are continually fed in.
2 A batch process is where the whole process takes a limited time then stops and can be changed if necessary.
3 Any three from: research and testing, labour, energy, raw materials, time taken for development, marketing costs.
4 Any two from: there are legal requirements, investment costs of its research and development, raw materials, expensive extraction from plants, it is labour intensive.

Page 38
1 Diamond, graphite and buckminster fullerene.
2 Conducts electricity and has a high melting point.
3 Working at the level of atoms.
4 The properties of large amounts of a material.

Page 39
1 Any three from: lakes, rivers, aquifers, reservoirs.
2 To filter out fine particles that do not sediment out.
3 A precipitation reaction.
3 Silver nitrate.

C5 How much?

Page 41
1 30.
2 90.
3 46.
4 C_3H_7.

Page 42
1 Pb^{2+}, I^-.
2 Negative ions (cations).
3 Anode dissolves.
4 Current and time.

Page 43
1 RDA is the amount of nutrient that it is suggested different types of people eat.
2 A substance that dissolves in a liquid.
3 The taste will be too strong.
4 90 cm^3.

Page 44
1 Blue.
2 It increases.
3 Burette and pipette.
4 To increase the reliability.

Page 45
1 Gas syringe, upturned burette.
2 17 cm^3.
3 22 cm^3.
4 Only half the mass of Mg was used in reaction 2, so only half the volume of gas was produced.

Page 46
1 $\rightleftharpoons$
2 To the right.
3 Sulfur trioxide.
4 450 °C, atmospheric pressure, catalyst of vanadium pentoxide, V_2O_5.

Page 47
1 A strong acid has a lower pH than a weak acid./A strong acid reacts faster than a weak acid.
2 Not all molecules separate into ions.
3 60 cm^3.
4 H^+.

Page 48
1 Yellow.
2 Silver nitrate + sodium iodide → silver iodide + sodium nitrate.
3 Mix solutions of silver nitrate and sodium chloride. Filter. Wash the precipitate with distilled water. Dry the precipitate.
4 To remove traces of the solution filtered with the precipitate.

C6 Chemistry out there

Page 50
1 It forms water when reacted with oxygen.
2 Petrol reserves will eventually run out. More laws are being passed to reduce the pollution from exhausts.
3 Relights a glowing splint.
4 Heat is given out.

Page 51
1 Any three from: cover the iron with oil or grease/paint/tin plate/a layer of zinc (galvanising) or sacrifice another metal in sacrificial protection/alloy with other elements.
2 Prevents oxygen or water reaching the surface of the iron.
3 A reaction is taking place/tin is being displaced.
4 Zinc + iron nitrate → zinc nitrate + iron.

Page 52
1 Sugars, enzymes from yeast and one from water/temperature between 25 and 50 °C/no oxygen.
2 Glucose → ethanol + carbon dioxide.
3 Can be made from ethene.
4 Hot aluminium oxide catalyst.

Page 53
1 Sodium and chlorine.
2 Using underground cutting machines. Pumping water down a borehole, dissolving the salt, pumping to surface and evaporating.
3 Any three from: sterilise drinking water supplies, to make bleach/solvents/plastics.
4 Separates the products.

Page 54
1 An increased risk of getting sunburnt/'ageing' skin/increase risk of skin cancer/cataracts of the eyes.
2 They increase.
3 Refrigerants and aerosol propellants.
4 Chlorine free radicals attack ozone molecules, turning the ozone back into oxygen gas and depleting the ozone layer.

Page 55
1 Permanent hardness.
2 Rainwater is acidic.
3 Weak acid.
4 Both kinds of hardness.

Page 56
1 Vegetable oils.
2 Bromine water is orange and is decolourised when shaken with an unsaturated compound/ it loses its colour.
3 A water-in-oil emulsion.
4 Vegetable oils are heated in large vats with sodium hydroxide solution.

Page 57
1 Aspirin, paracetamol and ibuprofen.
2 Can cause liver damage.
3 Aspirin relieves pain/lowers the body temperature, so reducing fever/it thins the blood, which helps prevent blood clots forming.
4 $C_{13}H_{18}O_2$.

Workbook answers

Remember:
Check which grade you are working at.

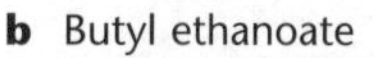

Fundamental concepts

Page 62

1 a i A and B **ii** C and D
b i Magnesium + oxygen; ⟶ magnesium oxide
$2Mg + O_2 \longrightarrow 2MgO$
2 a i 3 **ii** 6 **iii** 1 Cu, 1 S, 4 O
b 9
3 a H_2, S, O_2, Cu **b** H_2O, $CuSO_4$ **c** H_2, O_2, H_2O, $CuSO_4$
4 a i 2 **ii** 4 **iii** 2 **iv** 3
b CH_3COOH or $C_2H_4O_2$ **c** ionic

C1 Carbon chemistry

Page 63 Cooking

1 a Barbeque; in a grill; on an electric/gas ring (frying, boiling or steaming); in a microwave; in an oven *(Any 3 = 1 mark each)*
b The food needs high temperature to kill harmful microbes in food; the texture of food is improved; the taste of food is improved; the flavour of food is enhanced; food is easier to digest *(Any 2 = 1 mark each)*
2 a Irreversible; energy; substance
b They change shape
3 a Baking powder; carbon dioxide; heated
b i Sodium hydrogencarbonate ⟶ sodium carbonate + carbon dioxide + water
ii Sodium hydrogencarbonate
iii Sodium carbonate/carbon dioxide/water *(Any 1)*
4 Colourless; milky (cloudy)

Page 64 Food additives

1 a Chemicals
b Antioxidants; food colours; emulsifiers; flavour enhancers
c Stop food from reacting with oxygen and turning bad
d It was found to be harmful to some children
e Tinned fruit and wine
f Preserve food from reacting with oxygen and preventing bacteria or mould; to give a different sensory experience such as enhancing the colour/flavour of food *(Any 1 = 1 mark)*
2 a

ingredient	typical value per 100g
wheat	14.0 g
sugar	6.0 g
salt	0.2 g

(Wheat before sugar = 1 mark; sugar before salt = 1 mark)

b To stop food spoiling
c Packaging that changes the condition of the food to extend its shelf life
d Packaging that uses sensors to monitor the quality of the food and lets the customer know when the food is no longer fresh
3 a Detergent
b A detergent in washing-up liquid provides 'hooks' between oil and water; the oil is 'hooked' on to the water and pulled off a dirty plate; the detergent in washing-up liquid acts as an emulsifier; the tail is a 'fat-loving' part and the head is a 'water-loving' part; the fat-loving part of the molecule goes into the oil and attracts it towards this end; the water-loving part will not go in; the water-loving part stays out of the oil but is attracted to the water molecules; the oil is 'hooked-up' to the water
c Some paints; milk; mayonnaise *(Any 1 = 1 mark each)*

Page 65 Smells

1 a Rose; lavender **b** Distilled
c i Animals have no control over what is happening to them
ii They feel safer if the cosmetics have been tested
2 a

evaporate easily	it can be put directly on the skin
non-toxic	its particles can reach the nose
insoluble in water	it does not poison people
does not irritate the skin	it cannot be washed off easily

b Sense cells in the nose
3 a i Acid + alcohol ⟶ ester + water
(reactants = 1 mark, products = 1 mark)
ii *(Alcohol and acid label = 1 mark)*
iii *(Label to upward condenser tube = 1 mark)*
iv At X the vapour is cooling down again and condensing back to a liquid
v So that the mixture can be boiled/react for longer (without drying out)
b Butyl ethanoate
4 a Insoluble; soluble **b** Solution

Page 66 Making crude oil useful

1 a Coal; gas; crude oil
b Formed from dead animals and/or plants; trapped in the Earth; and compressed over millions of years
c When these fossil fuels are used up there will be no more
d Because they are no longer being made
2 a Boiling point
b A molecule containing carbon and hydrogen only
c i *(A: at the bottom, left-hand side, of the tower = 1 mark)*
ii *(B: it 'exits' through the bottom of the tower = 1 mark)*
iii *(C: at the top of the tower = 1 mark)*
iv Fractions with lower boiling points such as petrol/LPG
3 a i It is pumped using oil rigs and goes through pipelines
ii The oil spills and forms an oil slick
b Increase in wealth in population and therefore an increase in number of cars on roads
4 a High temperature; a catalyst
b C_7H_{16}

Page 67 Making polymers

1 a Polymers; chains; monomers; polymerisation **b** C
c High pressure; catalyst
2 a Carbon; hydrogen *(Both = 1 mark)* **b** D
c i An alkane has a single bond, C–C **ii** Propene
d i Contains an oxygen atom **ii** It contains a double bond
iii A polymer (made from the monomer butene)

Page 68 Designer polymers

1 a Fabrics for clothes; paint for cars; cases for computers; packaging; insulating or any other reasonable use *(Any 2 = 2 marks)*
b Poly(ethene); nylon; polyester; polystyrene; poly(propene) *(Any 2 = 2 marks)*
c Flexible – to allow insulating/non-conducting or able to be coloured
d Keeps people dry not only from the rain but also from sweat
e It keeps water vapour from body sweat in, the water vapour from the sweat condenses and makes the wearer wet and cold inside their raincoat
f

polymer	property 1	property 2	use
PVC	waterproof	flexible	raincoat
poly(ethene)	waterproof	flexible	plastic bags
poly(styrene)	rigid	absorbs shock	packaging
poly(propene)	strong	flexible	ropes

2 a They do not decay and are not decomposed by bacteria
b Landfill sites: waste valuable land; burning: toxic gases; recycling: difficulty in sorting different polymers *(1 mark each = 3 marks)*
c i So that they do not have to be disposed of in landfill sites; burned but can decay by bacterial action
ii To make laundry bags for hospitals so that they degrade when washed leaving the laundry in the machine *(Or any other suitable use)*

Page 69 Using carbon fuels

1 a Petrol; it flows around an engine
b i Coal **ii** High energy value; good availability
2 a Oxygen **b** Carbon dioxide; water
c Monoxide; toxic; blue; yellow; monoxide; soot; water vapour; less
d i Hydrocarbon fuel + oxygen ⟶ carbon dioxide + water
ii Carbon dioxide; water
iii Carbon dioxide turns limewater milky/white; copper sulfate turns blue with water *(Any 1 = 2 marks)*

Page 70 Energy

1 a Heat; light; sound; electrical *(Any order)*
b Exothermic; endothermic; exothermic; exothermic
2 a i Oxygen
ii Ethanol + oxygen ⟶ carbon dioxide + water
iii Ethanol and oxygen

b i

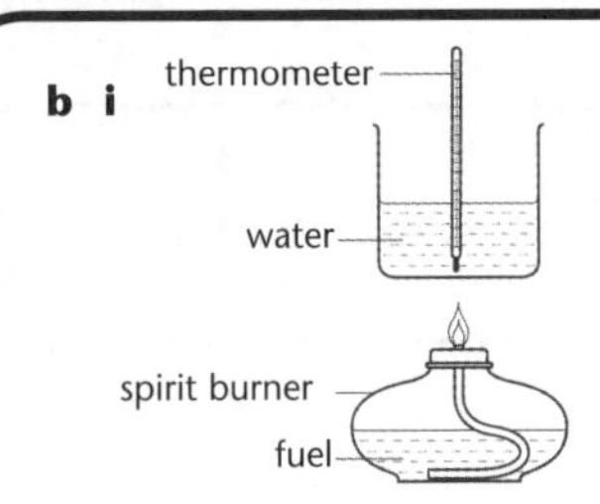

ii The mass of fuel; increase in temperature; mass of water
iii The same mass of fuel; same increase in temperature; same mass of water *(Any 1)*

C2 Rocks and metals

Page 72 Paints and pigments

1 a To decorate surfaces; to protect surfaces
b i Pigment; binding medium; solvent
ii The tiny particles of pigment powder are spread through the oil; a mixture of solid dispersed in a liquid is called a colloid
c Made of tiny droplets of one liquid in water which is called an emulsion; when emulsion paint has been painted onto a surface as a thin layer; the water evaporates leaving the binding medium and pigment behind; as it dries it joins together to make a continuous film *(Any 2)*
2 a i It changes colour **ii** It changes back to the original colour
b Phosphorescent
c Many people find that anything over 60 °C is too hot to hold so it can be used to paint cups; used to paint kettles; to act as a warning
3 a The juice of coloured berries
b They give a brighter colour; it does not fade as much as a natural dye
c Over the past 150 years chemists have been making man-made (synthetic) dyes; these give brighter colour and do not fade as much as a natural dye; give a wider range of colours

Page 73 Construction materials

1 a Granite; marble; limestone *(Or any reasonable material from rock)*
b Aluminium; iron (steel) *(Or any reasonable metal)*
c Limestone; marble; granite.
d

building material	**brick**	**cement**	**glass**	**iron**	**aluminium**
raw material	clay	limestone and clay	sand	iron ore	aluminium

2 Quarries and mines take up land-space; quarrying means an increase in noise, traffic and dust; landscapes are destroyed and have to be reconstructed
3 a Limestone; marble *(Accept chalk)*
b Thermally decomposes
c Cement, sand, and gravel are mixed with water and left to set
d It is much stronger than normal concrete
e Steel rods are put inside it; the concrete is poured around steel rods and left to set; it is therefore made of two materials
f Calcium carbonate ⟶ calcium oxide + carbon dioxide *(Each compound = 1 mark)*

Page 74 Does the Earth move?

1 a

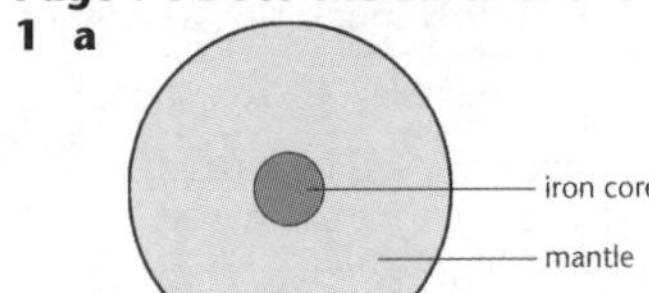

b Molten rock
c Tectonic plates; earthquakes; volcanoes
d Less dense **e** Continental; oceanic
2 a i Igneous **ii** Lava
iii Runny lava is fairly safe, thick lava can be given out violently and catastrophically
iv Volcanic soil is very fertile
b If the magma is less dense than the crust
c

small crystals
cool rapidly
basalt

large crystals
cool slowly
granite

Page 75 Metals and alloys

1 a Compound; element; carbon
b It is cheaper to recycle copper than extract new copper from the ground; recycling also saves the energy needed to crush rock and to operate smelters and electrolysis cells
c It must first be analysed to find out how much of each element is present
d It has to be electrolysed again before it can be used
2 a Impure copper which dissolves into the electrolyte
b It is 'plated' with new copper
3 a It is a mixture of a metal element with another element
b

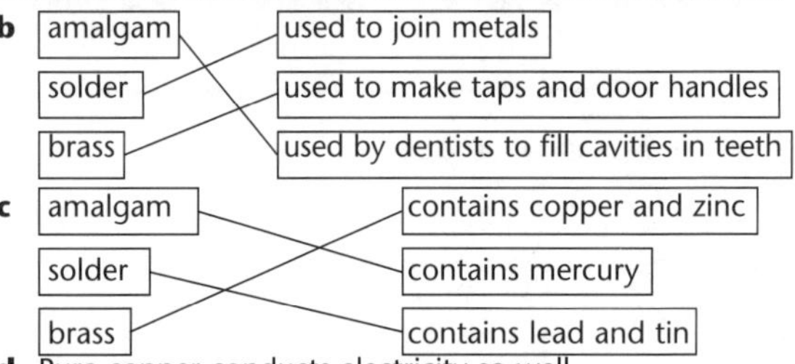

c
d Pure copper conducts electricity so well

Page 76 Cars for scrap

1 a Oxygen; water
b Salt accelerates rusting which means that car bodies rust quicker
c It has a protective layer of aluminium oxide which does not flake off the surface
d It flakes off
2 a

fibres glass
metals plastics

b

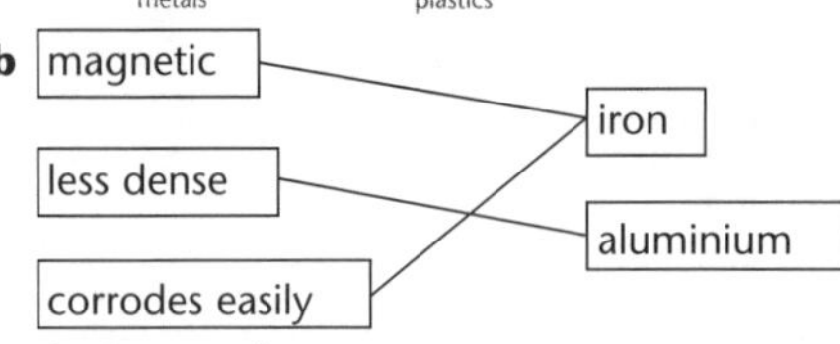

c i Iron; carbon
ii Stronger; harder; does not rust as easily as pure iron *(Any 2)*
iii Advantages: the mass of a car body made of aluminium will be less than the same car body made from steel; the car body made of aluminium will corrode less; disadvantage: the car body of the same car will be more expensive made from aluminium
d The car body is cut into smaller pieces and an electromagnet is used to attract iron or steel
3 More recycling of metals means that less metal ore needs to be mined; recycling of iron and aluminium saves money and energy compared to making iron from their ores; less crude oil is used to make plastics; less non-biodegradeable waste from plastics is dumped; recycling batteries reduces the dumping of toxic materials into the environment *(Any 3)*

Page 77 Clean air

1 a Oxygen; nitrogen; carbon dioxide *(Any order)*
b

increases the level of carbon dioxide and decreases the level of oxygen — combustion, respiration
photosynthesis — decreases the level of carbon dioxide and increases the level of oxygen

c i *(See diagram)*
ii *(See diagram)*
iii Combustion and respiration increase the level of carbon dioxide and decrease the level of oxygen; photosynthesis decreases the level of carbon dioxide and increases the level of oxygen

0.035% carbon dioxide
0.965% water vapour
21% oxygen
78% nitrogen

2 a In volcanoes
b These organisms could remove carbon dioxide from the atmosphere and add oxygen; eventually the level of oxygen reached what it is today
3 a

pollutant	**carbon monoxide**	**oxides of nitrogen**	**sulfur dioxide**
environmental problem	*a poisonous gas*	photochemical smog and acid rain	acid rain that kills plants and aquatic life, erodes stonework and corrodes metals
origin of pollutant	incomplete combustion of petrol or diesel in car engine	*formed in the internal combustion engine*	*formed when sulfur impurities in fossil fuels burn*

b It changes carbon monoxide into carbon dioxide and oxides of nitrogen into nitrogen.

Page 78 Faster or slower (1)

1 a 33 seconds
 b No more gas is made or the reactants have run out
 c 33 cm^3

2 If the concentration/temperature/pressure/surface area is increased then the rate of reaction increases

3 a *(See graph)*

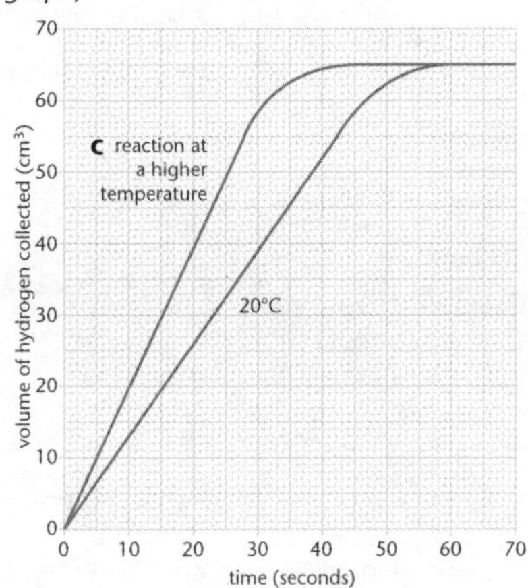

 b Gradient **C**, the higher temperature, has the steeper gradient
 c As the temperature increases the particles move faster; the reacting particles have more kinetic energy and so the number of collisions increases and the number of successful collisions increases

Page 79 Faster or slower (2)

1 a A reaction that takes place very quickly
 b Burning hydrogen; custard powder; TNT/dynamite explosion *(Any 2)*
 c Carbon dioxide; water vapour

2 a Powdered reactant will react faster; as the surface area increases; there are more collisions between reacting particles
 b Carbon dioxide is given off
 c i 25–27 seconds ii *(See graph)*

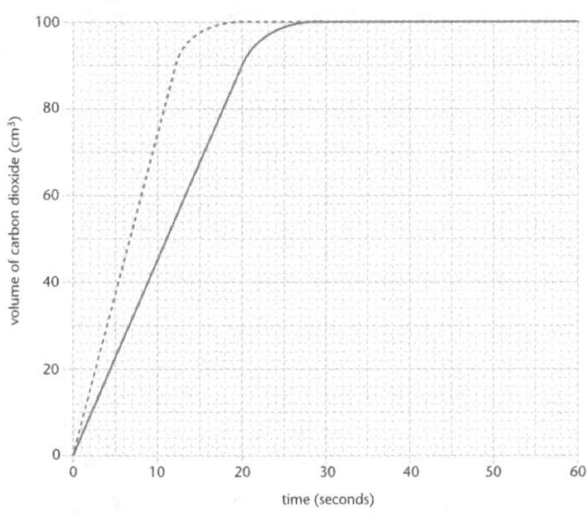

  iii As there is a greater surface area there are more frequent collisions between particles

3 a A chemical that speeds up (changes the rate of) a reaction but remains unchanged at the end of the reaction
 b Only small amounts of it are needed; it remains unchanged at the end of the reaction

C3 The periodic table

Page 81 What are atoms like?

1 a i *(See diagram)*

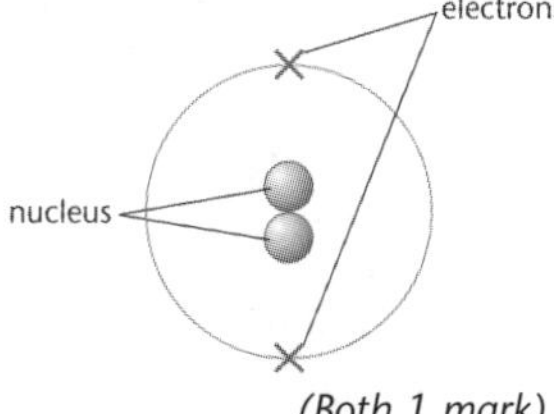

  ii Because it has the same number of positive charges in the nucleus as there are negatively charged electrons around it

 b Protons; neutrons *(Both 1 mark)*
 c

	relative charge	relative mass
electron	–1	0.0005 (zero)
proton	+1	1
neutron	0	1

 d The number of protons in an atom
 e The total number of protons and neutrons in an atom

2 a Phosphorus
 b 20
 c A substance that cannot be broken down chemically
 d There are just over 100 elements in the periodic table
 e A substance that contains at least two elements that are chemically joined together
 f Isotopes are elements that have the same atomic number but different mass numbers

Page 82 Ionic bonding

1 a

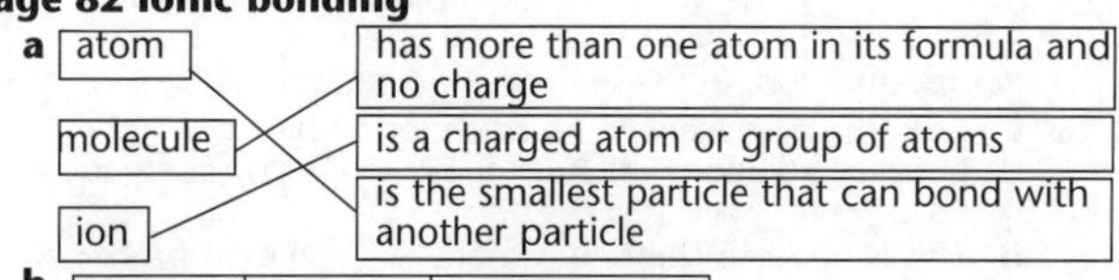

 b

atom	ion	molecule
O	Na^+	H_2
H	Cl^-	NaOH
Mg	SO_4^{2-}	$MgSO_4$

2 a i An atom has extra electrons in its outer shell and needs to lose them to be stable
 b *(See diagram)*

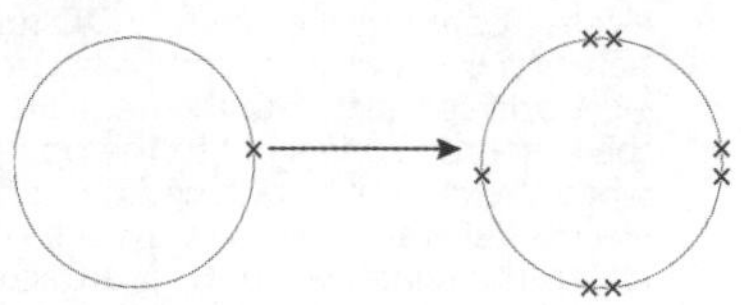

 c i Positive
  ii Sodium/lithium/ potassium
 d i Gaining
  ii Fluorine/chlorine/bromine/iodine
 e Positive; negative; lattice

3 a Have a high melting point
 b Sodium chloride solution; molten (melted) magnesium oxide; molten sodium chloride

Page 83 Covalent bonding

1 a Three b Two

2 a Covalent bonding
 b A molecule of water is made up of three atoms, two hydrogen and one oxygen; oxygen has six electrons in its outer shell; it needs two more electrons to be complete; hydrogen atoms each have one electron in their only shell; the oxygen outer shell is shared with each of the hydrogen electrons; each of the hydrogen atoms has a share of two more electrons making the shell full
 c Because they are covalently bonded; there are no free electrons

3 a i Group 1 ii Sodium; potassium
 b Sodium; silicon; sulphur
 c The group number is the same as the number of electrons in the outer shell; it has 1 electron in the outer shell
 d 7
 e i 2
  ii It is in the second row down because the first two electrons are in the first shell and the next 7 electrons are in the second shell; fluorine electrons occupy two shells so it is in the second period

Page 84 The group 1 elements

1 a They react with air and water
 b i Their density is less than the density of water
  ii Hydrogen
 c Sodium + water ⟶ sodium hydroxide + hydrogen
 d Potassium, sodium, lithium
 e

	melting point in °C	boiling point in °C
$_{3}Li$	179	1317
$_{11}Na$	98	892
$_{19}K$	64	774

 f They each have one electron in their outer shell so they react in a similar way

2 a red – lithium; yellow – sodium; lilac – potassium
 b They moistened a flame test wire; with dilute hydrochloric acid; they dipped the flame test wire into the sample of solid chemical; they held the flame test wire in a blue Bunsen burner flame

Page 85 The group 7 elements

1 a i Chlorine is used to sterilise water
  ii Iodine is used to sterilise wounds
 b A preservative; a flavouring; in the manufacture of chlorine *(Any 2)*

2 a

chlorine	green gas
iodine	grey solid

b They all have seven electrons in their outer shell

c

Reactivity ↑

$_{9}F$
$_{17}Cl$
$_{35}Br$
$_{53}I$

d Potassium + iodine ⟶ potassium iodide

3 a i Chlorine displaces the bromide ions which become bromine solution which is red-brown/a displacement reaction occurs

ii This is because chlorine is more reactive than bromine/ bromine does not displace the chloride ions

b i Bromine + potassium iodide ⟶ potassium bromide + iodine

ii $Br_2 + 2KI \longrightarrow 2KBr + I_2$

Page 86 Electrolysis

1 Electrolysis; electrolyte; anode; cathode; anode; cathode; negative; positive

2 a The electrolyte is a dilute solution of sulfuric acid; two electrodes are connected to a DC source of electric current, between 6 V and 12 V, and placed into the electrolyte; the electrode connected to the negative terminal is the cathode; the electrode connected to the positive terminal is the anode; when the current is switched on bubbles of gas appear at both electrodes; water splits into two ions: H^+ is the positive ion and OH^- is the negative ion; H^+ is attracted to the negative cathode and discharged as hydrogen gas, H_2; OH^- is attracted to the positive anode and discharged as oxygen gas, O_2 *(Any 6)*

b Because the formula of the compound breaking up is H_2O

3 a Lighted splint burns with a 'pop' in hydrogen

b A glowing splint relights in oxygen

4 a The ore of aluminium oxide is bauxite; aluminium oxide is melted; aluminium is formed at the graphite cathode; oxygen is formed at the graphite anode; the anodes are gradually worn away by oxidation; this forms carbon dioxide; the process requires a high electrical energy input *(Any 4)*

b Aluminium oxide ⟶ aluminium + oxygen

Page 87 Transition elements

1 a Conduct heat; are shiny; conduct electricity; are sonorous (ring when struck); are malleable; are ductile

b i Copper compounds are blue

ii Iron(II) compounds are pale green

iii Iron(III) compounds are orange/brown.

c i Iron is used in the Haber process to make ammonia

ii Nickel is a transition metal; because it is in the transition metal block

2 A precipitation reaction

3 a Thermal decomposition

b copper carbonate ⟶ copper oxide + carbon dioxide

4

ion	colour
Cu^{2+}	form a blue gelatinous solid
Fe^{2+}	form a grey/green gelatinous solid
Fe^{3+}	form an orange gelatinous solid

Page 88 Metal structure and properties

1 a i C **ii** B **iii** C **b** A **c** Lustrous; malleable

d It has high thermal conductivity and is malleable; it is also resistant to attack by oxygen or acids

2 a

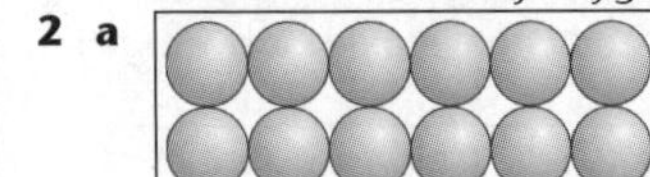

b The particles are close together; in a regular arrangement

3 a Very low temperatures

b Materials that conduct electricity with little or no resistance

c Loss-free power transmission; super-fast electronic circuits; powerful electromagnets

C4 Chemical economics

Page 90 Acids and bases

1 a i Neutralisation

ii The manufacture of fertilisers; cleaning metals; car battery acids *(Any 2)*

b i A base when it dissolves in water **ii** Acid; water

c Copper carbonate + sulfuric acid ⟶ copper sulfate + water + carbon dioxide

d The salt formed is sodium nitrate

2 a i Strong acid **ii** Strong alkali

b Increases from a low number to 7 on neutralisation; then from 7 to a higher number if excess alkali is added

c The pH at the start is high, colour is purple; the pH falls as the acid neutralises the alkali, colour changes to blue; when neutral, the pH = 7, colour is green

Page 91 Reacting masses

1 a i 56 **ii** 23 + 16 + 1 = 40 **iii** 40 + 12 + (16 × 3) = 100

b 40 + 2 (16 + 1) = 40 + (2 × 17) = 74

c i The reaction has given off a gas

ii Oxygen from the air has probably reacted with the chemical

d In filtration: small amounts stay on the filter paper; in evaporation: some chemicals spit out into the room; in transferring liquids: tiny amounts of liquid stick to the sides of the beaker because more than one reaction might be taking place so the reactants are being used up in a different reaction *(Any 2)*

2 a 28 **b** 42

c $\dfrac{\text{Actual yield}}{\text{Percentage yield}} \times 100$

d $\dfrac{28 \times 100}{42} = 66\%$

Page 92 Fertilisers and crop yield

1 a Minerals through its roots

b Nitrogen (N); phosphorus (P); potassium (K)

c Fertilisers **d** To increase their crop yields

e They are dissolved in water so they can be absorbed by plants through their roots

f $(NH_4)_2SO_4$ Mr = 2(14 + 4) + 32 + (16 × 4) = 132

2 a C D B A

b A: water is evaporated off to leave crystals; B: the crystals are filtered off; C: alkali is measured and put into a flask; D: acid is added from a burette to an alkali

c Water

d i Phosphoric acid

ii Ammonium hydroxide

iii Phosphoric acid + ammonium hydroxide ⟶ ammonium phosphate + water

Page 93 The Haber process

1 a Ammonia **b** The air **c** Reversible reaction

2 Nitrogen is obtained from the air; hydrogen comes from natural gas; the gases are passed over an iron catalyst under high pressure; an optimum temperature of 450 °C is chosen; there is a recycling system for unreacted nitrogen and hydrogen *(Any 3)*

3 a The cost of building the plant; people's wages; the cost of the raw materials; nitrogen and hydrogen and the energy costs; how quickly the new substance can be made (cost of a catalyst) *(Any 3)*

b

factor	explanation
cost of building the plant	The bigger the plant the longer it takes to repay so putting up cost of fertiliser
people's wages	Constant cost added to cost of fertiliser
cost of the raw materials	Constant cost added to cost of fertiliser
energy costs	The higher the pressure used the more energy needed as a cost added to cost of fertilser
how quickly the new substance can be made	The quicker it can be made the less the cost of energy and people's wages needed

(Any 3)

c 400 atmospheres **d** Increases **e** Decreases

Page 94 Detergents

1 a

active detergent	to soften hard water
water softener	to give a whiter than white appearance
bleaches	to remove food stains at low temperatures
optical brighteners	to do the cleaning
enzymes	to remove coloured stains

b Organic acid + alkali ⟶ detergent (salt) + water

c It dissolves grease stains; it dissolves in water at the same time

d i It is better to wash clothes at 40 °C instead of at high temperatures because washing machines have to heat up a lot of water; this needs energy; so the lower the temperature of the water the less energy is used and less greenhouse gases are released into the atmosphere

ii As many dyes are easily damaged by high temperatures; it also means that many more fabrics can be machine washed as their structure would be damaged at higher temperatures

2 Solvents; solute; solution; soluble; insoluble

3 a Dry-cleaned

b It does not mean that no liquids are used, just that the liquid solvent is not water

Page 95 Batch or continuous?

1 a i Speciality chemicals, such as medicines and pharmaceutical drugs, are often made on demand in a batch process
ii Bulk chemicals such as ammonia
b Need to be made for a smaller demand; sterile conditions required so need to re-clean, need to change type of drug produced *(Any 1)*
c If a chemical is needed in large amounts it is usually made by a continuous process which can be more highly automated

2 a Extracted from plants
b Chemicals are held in the plant cells; plant cells have tough walls, so to extract the compound the plant is crushed to break the cell walls; then the chemical must be dissolved. This only works if a suitable solvent is used; the solvent dissolves lots of different compounds, so the desired compound is then separated from the others; this can be done by chromatography *(Any 4)*

3 a Research and testing; labour costs; energy costs; raw materials; development time *(Any 3)*
b

strict safety laws	The medicines are made by a batch process so less automation can be used.
research and development	They may be rare and costly
raw materials	They take years to develop
labour intensive	People need to be feel a benefit without too many side effects

Page 96 Nanochemistry

1 a

	diamond	graphite	buckminster fullerene
appearance	lustrous and colourless	*black solid*	black and opaque
solubility	*insoluble in water*	*insoluble in water*	*deep red solution in petrol*
electrical conductivity	*does not conduct electricity*	conducts electricity	conducts electricity
uses	cutting tools/ jewellery	electrodes/pencil lead/lubricant	semiconductors in electrical circuits
reasons for use	very hard/lustrous and colourless	conduct electricity/ high melting point/ slipppery and black/ slippery	*can join together to make nanotubes*

b

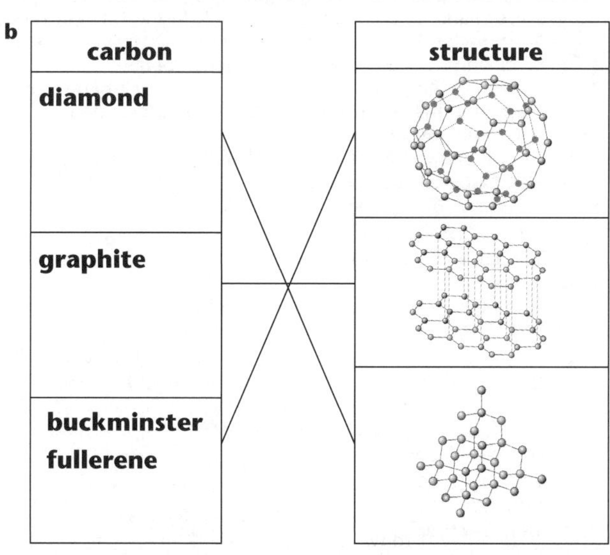

2 a Deep red
b i Very strong; conduct electricity
ii Semiconductors in electrical circuits; industrial catalysts; reinforcement of graphite in tennis rackets *(Any 2)*

Page 97 How pure is our water?

1 a Lakes; rivers; aquifers; reservoirs.
b A cheap raw material; a coolant; a valuable solvent *(Any 2)*
c Dissolved salts and minerals; pollutants; insoluble materials; microbes (killed by chlorination) *(Any 2)*
d Nitrate residues; lead compounds; pesticide residues *(Any 2)*
e Clean water saves more lives than medicines

2 Sedimentation → filtration → chlorination
Sedimentation: larger bits drop to the bottom; filtration: sand is used to filter out finer particles; chlorination: kills microbes

3 a

chlorides	white precipitate
iodides	yellow precipitate

b Barium chloride solution
c Lead nitrate + potassium chloride ⟶ lead chloride + potassium nitrate

C5 How much?

Page 99 Moles and empirical formulae

1 a 18 b 101 c 132

2 a Keiko is correct because mass is conserved in a chemical reaction/the total mass before a reaction is the same as the total mass after a reaction b 0.44 g
c 1.62 g [2.5 is (125/100) × 2; (81/100) × 2 is 1.62]

3 a 5.6 g MgO is made. [$2Mg + O_2 \rightarrow 2MgO$]
b 32 g oxygen c 2.3 g Na

4 a The simplest whole number ratio of each type of atom in a compound. b CH_2O

Page 100 Electrolysis

1 a i & ii

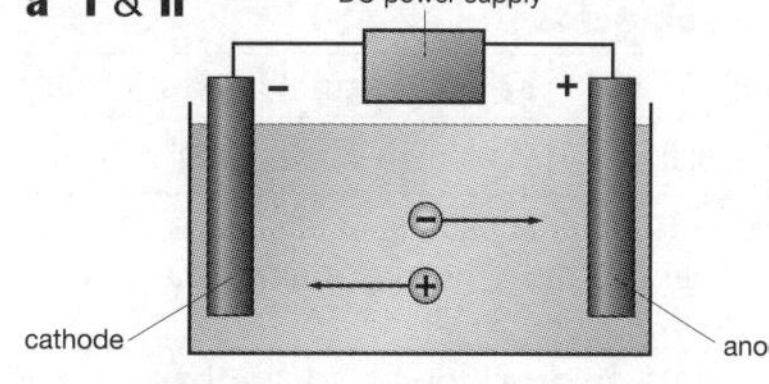

b Electrolysis is the decomposition of a liquid by passing an electric current through it, where the negative ions are attracted to the positive electrode and the positive ions are attracted to the negative electrode
c Hydrogen and oxygen

2 a i It increases ii It decreases b Both

3 a So that the ions; are free to move
b

molten electrolyte	at the cathode	at the anode
Al_2O_3	aluminium	oxygen
$PbBr_2$	lead	bromine
PbI_2	lead	iodine
KCl	potassium	chlorine

Page 101 Quantitative analysis

1 a 12.2 g b 10 g c 50%
d To halve their intake of saturated fat; as too much is linked with risk of heart disease

2 a 1000 cm^3 b 0.75 dm^3 c 20 cm^3

3 a Babies milk solution needs to be at the exact concentration otherwise nutrients are at the wrong level or digestive problems can occur
b More crowded particles
c She would add 90 cm^3 water; and add 10 cm^3 of acid solution

Page 102 Titrations

1 a **A** pH is high-alkali; **B** pH begins to fall as acid is added; **C** all the alkali is neutralised, pH is 7; D excess acid, pH is below 7
b 24 cm^3 c 1.6
d Acid and alkali neutralise making a salt and water only

2 a i

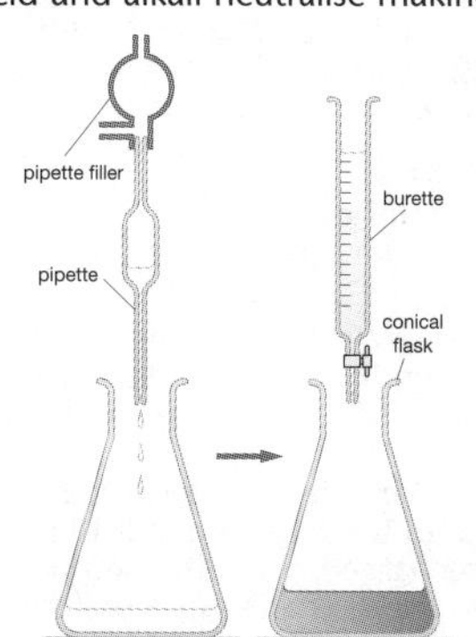

ii She wears safety goggles and pipettes a fixed volume of alkali into a flask; she puts a few drops of indicator into the flask; she slowly adds the acid from the burette into the flask swirling the contents; when the indicator suddenly changes the colour she notes the reading-then repeats the procedure until the volumes of acid are (almost) the same
b 27.0 cm^3 c To get consistent results

Page103 Gas volumes

1 a Measuring cylinder, burette **b** Mass of contents decreasing

c He puts a flask on the balance and adds marble chips, he puts a loose plug of cotton wool in the mouth of the flask, he records the mass; he then adds a fixed volume of dilute acid and records the mass of the contents every 30 s; the mass will decrease as gas is given off

d She adds magnesium to a flask and connects the syringe to the bung that will fit the flask; she then adds a fixed volume of dilute acid and quickly puts the bung in the mouth of the flask; she records the volume of gas produced every 10 s as the gas is given off

2 a 22 cm^3 **b** 56–60 s. The magnesium was all used up **c** 16 cm^3 **d** 11 cm^3 **e** She only used half the mass of Mg

Page 104 Equilibria

1 a C → A + B **b** Reversible

c The rate of the forward reaction equals the rate of the backward reaction **d** It lies to the right

2 a 50% **b** Increases **c** Decreases

3 a Contact **b** Sulfur; air; water

c i Sulfur dioxide; oxygen **ii** Reversible reaction **iii** Atmospheric pressure; temperature 450 °C; catalyst V_2O_5 **iv** Burning sulfur in oxygen

Page 105 Strong and weak acids

1 a

hydrochloric acid	nitric acid	ethanoic acid	sulphuric acid
strong	strong	weak	strong

b i pH of B is lower **ii** H^+ **iii** B ionises fully so that all the H^+ ions are available **iv** Reversible reaction

2 a & b

	hydrochloric acid	ethanoic acid
magnesium	hydrogen	hydrogen
calcium carbonate	carbon dioxide	carbon dioxide
speed of reaction	faster	slower

c HCl produces more available H^+ ions than ethanoic acid; so there are fewer collisions with H^+ ions from ethanoic acid, so a slower reaction

3 They produce the same amount of gas.

4 a There are fewer H^+ ions that can move

b H^+ are positive ions so are attracted to the negative electrode

Page 106 Ionic equations

1 a i Insoluble **ii** Ions **b** Ions are free to move

2 a

solution	chloride	bromide	iodide
colour of precipitate	white	cream	yellow

b Barium chloride

c i I^- or $AgNO_3$ **ii** AgI or NO_3^- **iii** (s) solid; (aq) aqueous

d Silver nitrate + sodium bromide → silver bromide + sodium nitrate

3 a

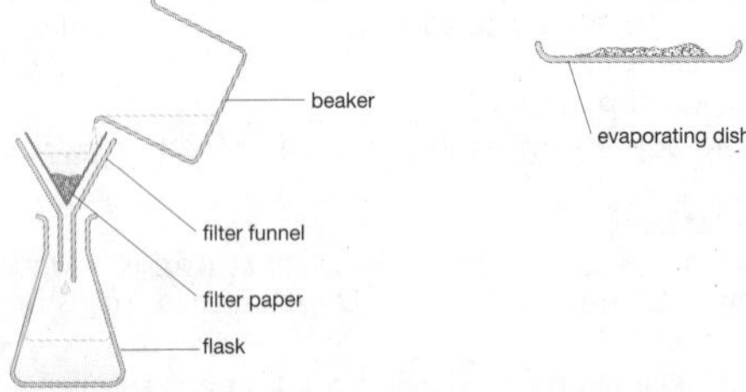

b Stage 1 Add the solutions together; **Stage 2** Filter the precipitate; **Stage 3** Wash the precipitate with distilled water; **Stage 4** Dry the precipitate

C6 Chemistry out there

Page 108 Energy transfers – fuel cells

1 a Pops with a lighted splint **b** Relights a glowing splint **c** Water **d** Exothermic

2 a Electrical **b i** Hydrogen + oxygen → water **ii** When hydrogen reacts with oxygen the chemical energy is converted directly into electrical energy, a potential difference is created

3 a Provides electrical power **b** They are efficient/they waste very little energy; they are lighter than normal batteries; they do not need time out to be recharged; the water produced is used by the astronauts *(Any 3)* **c i** The laws on pollution from carbon emissions are being tightened, there are no carbon emissions from the use of fuel cells; they are more efficient as no energy is lost as heat energy **ii** Hydrogen gas is difficult to store; not yet readily available *(Any 1)*

Page 109 Redox reactions

1 a Rust

b Hydrated iron(III) oxide

c Iron + water + oxygen → hydrated iron(III) oxide

2 a Paint; cover with oil/grease; galvanise; alloy; use sacrificial protection; tin plate **b** Paint; covering with grease/oil

3 a Magnesium is more reactive than zinc; which is more reactive than iron; which is more reactive than tin

b i Tin sulfate **ii** Zinc metal is less reactive than magnesium so does not displace it from solution **iii** Zinc + iron sulfate → zinc sulfate + iron

4 Reduction and oxidation occur at the same time

Page 110 Alcohols

1 a Solvent; alcoholic drink/beverage **b** The source of the sugar for fermentation can be grown again quickly

c Temperature 25–50 °C; presence of water; enzymes in yeast; absence of oxygen

d Glucose → carbon dioxide + ethanol **e** Distillation

f i C_2H_5OH **ii**

```
   H  H
   |  |
H—C—C—O—H
   |  |
   H  H
```

2 a Hydration **b i** Phosphoric acid **ii** Heated; catalyst **c** Ethene + water → ethanol

3 a Dehydration **b** Aluminium oxide (by the bung) **c** Ethanol → ethene + water

Page 111 Chemistry of sodium chloride (NaCl)

1 a It is an important raw material for the chemical industry **b** Cheshire **c** Subsidence

2 a Hydrogen **b** Bleached **c i** Inert electrodes **ii** Anode **iii** Sodium hydroxide

3 a Cathode **b** Chlorine

4 a Chlorine; and sodium hydroxide

b i Sodium hydroxide **ii** Make solvents; household bleach; plastics *(Any 2)* **iii** Bleach

Page 112 Depletion of the ozone layer

1 a Carbon; fluorine; chlorine

b They deplete the ozone layer and as they are so stable they are only slowly removed/last for years in the upper atmosphere; the ozone layer protects the Earth from excessive UV light

2 a O_3 **b** Cl **c** Free radical

d They are very stable and are only slowly removed, so last for years in the upper atmosphere

3 a Increased risk of sunburn; accelerated ageing of skin; increased risk of skin cancer; increased risk of cataracts *(Any 3)*

b Increased levels of UV light

4 a Alkanes or HFCs **b** 82%

Page 113 Hardness of water

1 a It does not lather well **b** Makes it slightly acidic

c Calcium carbonate + water + carbon dioxide → calcium hydrogencarbonate

2 a Calcium ions; and magnesium ions **b** Adding washing soda

c Ion exchange resins are in a column, the water flows over solid resin which has sodium ions on it; the resin traps the calcium and magnesium ions on to it, taking these ions out of the water and exchanging them for the sodium ions

3 a By boiling **b** Calcium hydrogencarbonate

4 a i C **ii** All of the other samples lather well/better with soap after boiling; they were either not hard or had temporary hardness

b Use the same volume of water; use the same volume of soap

Page 114 Natural fats and oils

1 a Bacon fat/ beef or lamb fat

b Olive oil/sunflower oil

c Vegetable oils to make biodiesel

2 a Esters

b i All the carbon–carbon bonds are single

ii The double bond

c i Shake bromine water with a sample of each hydrocarbon

ii With M, the brown bromine colour would stay; with N, the bromine would decolourise

3 a One liquid finely dispersed in another

b Water-in-oil emulsion

4 a Sodium hydroxide

b Saponification

Page 115 Analgesics

1 a Pharmacist

b Ibruprofen/paracetamol

2 $C_9H_8O_4$

3 a To reduce pain; to lower body temperature rapidly; to thin blood to reduce the risk of blood clots

b Can cause severe bleeding of the stomach

c It is faster acting and has fewer side effects

4 a Willow bark

b i It is an externally administered substance that modifies or affects chemical reactions in the body

ii Nothing else in the drug must be allowed to affect the body and cause other problems